*A
Harlequin
Romance*

OTHER
Harlequin Romances
by JANICE GRAY

SHAKE OUT
THE STARS

by

JANICE GRAY

HARLEQUIN BOOKS   TORONTO
WINNIPEG

First published in 1968 by Mills & Boon Limited,
50 Grafton Way, Fitzroy Square, London, England.

SBN 373-01275-6

© Janice Gray 1968

Harlequin Canadian edition published February, 1969
Harlequin U.S. edition published May, 1969

Reprinted 1971
Reprinted 1972
Reprinted 1975

Printed in Canada

CHAPTER I

It was raining. Not fast, but a tedious, all-enveloping drizzle that was somehow infinitely more depressing, since there really seemed no reason why it should not go on for ever. Linda Grierson, glancing out at the leaden sky, gave an involuntary sigh. Hateful, hateful climate! No wonder English people were always complaining about the weather. Goodness only knew they had something to complain about! It had been one of the wettest and coldest summers on record and it looked as though it was going to be followed by an equally wet and dreary autumn.

She allowed herself, for a few moments, to be lost in a dream that included blue skies, unlimited sunshine, the scent of water and green, green grass, before reluctantly returning to reality. She looked at her wristwatch and then with another small sigh, this time of relief, she began to tidy her desk and to put the cover on her typewriter. Five-and-twenty past five—almost time to go. Thank goodness, she thought, then almost immediately reproached herself. Surely she wasn't turning into a clock-watcher! Normally she was anything but: she was too interested in her job with a well-known publishing firm to be anything but generous with her time, but today she would be glad to get home. It had been one of those frightful days when nothing had seemed to go right. She had a thumping headache, too, and felt listless and tired. In actual fact she'd been off colour for quite a while now, and she had a cough that simply wouldn't go. She had almost made up her mind to go and see her doctor tomorrow. Perhaps he'd give her a tonic, something that would buck her up and give her a little more energy than she seemed to have at present. It wasn't likely that there was anything seriously wrong, it was probably just that she'd returned to work far too soon after that bad bout of 'flu. Ann, her flat-mate, had been horrified at the time, but her protests had fallen on deaf ears. After all, as Lin had pointed out, it wasn't as though there had been any chance of a pleasant convalescence, being cared for and cosseted. Not since Aunt Bea had died.

Lin sighed for a third time as she thought of the kind, warm-hearted aunt who had so generously given her a home when her own parents had been killed in an air-crash when she was only twelve years old. Aunt Bea had been a darling . . . she still missed her terribly. She missed ' home ', too . . . the ivy-covered cottage in the Cotswolds with its small, colourful garden, but of course Aunt Bea had only occupied it by virtue of her position as head-mistress of the little village school. Somebody else lived there now . . . somebody else woke up in the little gabled bedroom that had been Lin's. Somebody else lay in bed and listened to the thrushes and blackbirds singing outside the window, and smelt the fragrance of the honeysuckle which clustered over the front porch. April, her cousin, had hated the cottage and had always grumbled about its lack of modern amenities and its distance from what she called ' civilization ', but to Lin it had been perfection.

Then Aunt Bea had died after a sudden illness, and Lin and April, who were both eighteen, had been forced to find somewhere else to live. It had been April's idea, of course, that they should come to London. She'd always been crazy to leave home: the only reason she'd stayed as long as she had was because her mother had agreed to her enrolling at a drama school in Birmingham. Not that April could have cared very much about it, for when the blow had fallen she'd left immediately.

'We'll be able to pick and choose our jobs in London and of course the pay's *much* better!' she had told Lin, and rather against her better judgment Lin had allowed herself to be persuaded. She'd known, of course, that she at least wouldn't have difficulty in finding work, for she had had a good secretarial training. Aunt Bea had seen to that.

The door opened and Mr Heriot, for whom she worked, came into the room. He was carrying a sheaf of papers in his hand, and his face fell as he noticed the cover on the typewriter.

'Just off, Miss Grierson? Oh dear, I was rather hoping that you'd have time to make another copy of this report. I've suddenly realized I shall need one for first thing tomorrow morning.'

Lin stifled a groan. 'All right, Mr Heriot, I'll do it.' Another half-hour's work at least, she thought wearily. Oh well, it couldn't be helped.

Mr Heriot gave her a quick look. Unobservant though he usually was, something about Lin's small, pale face and shadowed eyes made him feel faintly uneasy. Come to think of it, the child hadn't looked at all well lately. She did her work as efficiently as ever, but she lacked vitality or enthusiasm. She had a nasty cough, too: he'd heard it often.

He said gruffly, ' You look tired, Miss Grierson. A holiday would do you good, but of course you've had your fortnight, haven't you? Where did you go?'

' To Cornwall. It rained cats and dogs every day,' Lin said wryly.

' H'm. Pity. Not that you'd have got much sun wherever you'd gone this year.' He hesitated. That report really was urgent. ' Sure you feel up to doing this extra work?'

' Of course.' With a smile that was almost convincing, Lin took the cover off her typewriter again and slid a sheet of paper, with its carbon and copy-sheet, into the carriage. She was a fast and accurate typist, but the report was long and complicated and it was well after six o'clock by the time she had finished and almost seven when she finally arrived home at the small flat in Maida Vale which she shared with Ann Janes.

' At last!' Ann, tall and dark and several years Lin's senior, came bustling into the sitting room from the tiny kitchenette as she heard Lin's key in the lock. ' I was beginning to think you were never coming! I've cooked something special for supper tonight: smell it?'

Lin sniffed obediently. The air was full of a rich, spicy fragrance: Ann was a wildly enthusiastic cook and whenever funds allowed was always trying out new and exotic recipes which she culled from the pages of women's magazines and the Sunday colour supplements.

'Been working overtime? You look fagged out, Lin.' Ann's keen eyes had taken in the weary slump of Lin's shoulders and the pallor of her small heart-shaped face. 'Here, sit down and drink this soup. It's scalding, though: watch out.'

Lin sank down into a chair. She felt almost too tired to eat, but she wouldn't have disappointed Ann for anything in the world. She picked up her spoon as Ann set a steaming bowl of soup before her.

'Smells gorgeous! Whose recipe is this, Ann?'

'One of Fanny Cradock's.' Ann sat down opposite Lin. 'Crépes Bon Viveur to follow, so eat up. Oh, and there's a letter for you from April, by the way. Up on the mantelpiece. No!—have your soup first!' as Lin made an instinctive move to get up. 'April's news will wait, food won't! I don't suppose her letter is anything more than a catalogue of her latest acquisitions, anyway. More model dresses and mink coats—if they wear mink coats in Tobago, that is!'

Lin laughed. 'I'm quite sure they'd be very much out of place. Don't be catty, Ann dear! Wouldn't you be thrilled with a model dress?'

'Not if I had to marry someone old enough to be my father to get one,' Ann said bluntly, and was immediately sorry when she saw Lin bite her lip. She was very fond of Lin, but had always disliked April. When the two cousins had first come to London they had all shared the same flat together for nearly a year, but last winter April had been invited by her wealthy godmother to accompany her on a Caribbean cruise. It was, as everyone had said, the

9

chance of a lifetime, and April had certainly made the most of it. While in Trinidad she had met, and subsequently married after a whirlwind courtship, a forty-five-year-old widower who owned extensive coconut plantations in Tobago. He also had a small daughter, Amanda, by his previous marriage, but she had been mentioned only rarely in April's first excited letters home. Godfrey Selby appeared to be a very wealthy man and he seemed to have delighted in showering his young wife with lavish and expensive gifts. April had sent them wonderful colour photographs of her new home, an impressive colonial-type mansion, and there'd been photographs, too, of Godfrey's enormous car . . . the small sports car he had bought April during the first week of their marriage . . . their yacht, their private swimming pool, their extensive grounds. They had spent their honeymoon in Florida, and April had written glowing accounts of the parties to which they had been invited, with frequent references to the gay and amusing people they'd met. 'Practically all millionaires, of course!' April had written.

Lin, who was an incurable romanticist, thought it was all rather like a Cinderella story come true and hoped (optimistically, Ann feared) that as in all good fairy tales April and her husband would live happily ever after. Ann was not so sure. She had no illusions about April, and felt fairly confident that she had married Godfrey Selby for money and not for love. She'd said as much to Lin and had nearly got her head bitten off for her pains. Lin was passionately loyal to her friends, and whatever her private misgivings about her cousin's actions nothing would ever have induced her to confide them to any-one else. Lin was true blue, Ann had thought rue-fully more than once. She wasn't a scrap like spoilt, selfish April: in fact, it would have been hard to find two cousins more unalike.

Now there was a look of relief on Lin's face as she said, ' I'm glad she's written. It's over two months since I last heard from her and I was beginning to feel a bit worried.'

Ann looked at her. This was too much, even from Lin! ' Worried? Lin, you *idiot*! Oh, I know you promised your aunt you'd look after her and all that, but she's *married* now! She's not your responsi-bility any longer, she's Godfrey Selby's!' Thank goodness, she added mentally. She'd always thought that April had imposed disgracefully on her cousin, deliberately exploiting Lin's loyalty and loving heart.

Lin sighed. ' I know. But . . . well, old habits die hard, I suppose.' She drank her soup quickly, burning the roof of her mouth, and jumping up to fetch her letter the moment she'd finished.

' I hope she's all right. I thought she sounded a bit depressed in her last letter, didn't you? Godfrey seems to work frightfully hard and April never has liked being left to her own devices.'

' Well, she couldn't have expected the honey-moon to last for ever! She had to come down to earth some time,' Ann said brutally. ' I suppose she's finding that even diamonds have their dis-advantages!'

' You're not fair, Ann!' Lin wild-catted to April's defence, just as the elder girl had known she would.

'She hasn't been married very long, of course she feels lonely when her husband's away from her!'

Ann looked sceptical, but she said nothing further. Lin had torn open the envelope and was already eagerly devouring its contents. Ann, watching her, saw a small worried frown appear on her forehead and her heart sank. She had seen that frown before . . . and it had always been on account of April, her moods, her follies or her extravagances. Oh, *damn* April, she thought. She saw Lin's pale cheeks flush suddenly and spoke sharply. 'What's the matter?'

Lin looked up from the letter, her eyes dazed and incredulous. 'Ann, she wants me to throw up my job and go and stay with her for a few weeks. She says she's lonely and she needs me badly.'

'We-e-ell!' Ann drew a long breath, her dark eyes snapping. 'Same old April, running true to form! What she wants, she must have! Has it ever occurred to her that you *like* your job? And that you might not want to throw it up? And what about your fare? Is April going to foot the bill for that?'

Lin flushed. 'She hasn't mentioned the fare.'

'I bet she hasn't!' Ann said grimly. 'Trust April to forget about a little thing like that! All the same, where on earth does she think you're going to find two hundred and fifty pounds at the drop of a hat?' She stopped suddenly, comprehension slowly dawning in her eyes. 'Oh, of course, your Aunt Bea's legacy! She left you three hundred pounds, didn't she?'

'Yes.' Lin spoke briefly. Aunt Bea had left her that small legacy for one reason, so that she should have a nest-egg to fall back on in an emergency.

Like most of her generation, Aunt Bea had been a great believer in nest-eggs for rainy days, and Lin had promised her that she would never touch the money without good reason.

Ann was still looking indignant, but at the same time her agile brain was exploring the situation from every possible angle. After a moment she said slowly, 'Of course you could do with a holiday just now, old thing, and I suppose Tobago is a pretty marvellous place in which to have one, judging from April's letters. But I honestly don't see why you should have to find the fare, Lin, when April's simply rolling! If she wants your company she should be prepared to pay for it!'

'Don't be silly, Ann! If I couldn't pay for myself I wouldn't go at all!' Lin said sharply. 'I wouldn't dream of accepting money from April! She knows that, or she should do!'

Ann groaned. 'Listen to her! Lin, you really are impossible! Haven't you been subsidizing April, on and off, ever since your aunt died? All the money her mother left her she squandered on clothes and that holiday in Greece and that film test and the modelling course and—oh yes, she *did* squander it, you know she did! You kept her when she wasn't working and you lent her nearly all your savings when she went off on that cruise last year! I thought she promised to pay you back, but I bet you haven't seen a penny! If after all that you don't feel you're entitled to a little something in return then you're a bigger idiot than I took you for!'

She paused for breath and Lin said quietly,

'You've forgotten something, Ann. Whatever I did for April was nothing compared with what her mother did for me for six years, remember.'

'Oh, I haven't forgotten! But why does that make you feel you're under an obligation to *April*?'

Lin side-stepped the question. 'She's all the family I've got, Ann. If she really is unhappy then of course I want to help her. Here, read what she says and tell me what you think,' and she handed over the two untidily-written sheets to her friend.

Ann read them in silence, her expression thoughtful as she came to the final paragraph. 'So please, Lin, do, do pack in that frightful dead-end job of yours and come and stay with me for a few weeks. Godfrey has had to go to New York: I don't suppose he'll be away for long, but even when he's here he's wrapped up in those boring old plantations of his, and I could do with your company. Actually things are rather horrid here at the moment—it's all a bit complicated, so I'll explain why when I see you! You will come, won't you? Please don't let me down!'

She laid the letter down without comment and looked at Lin, who was sitting with her chin cupped in her hands. The anxious frown had, if anything, deepened. What did April mean—'Things are rather horrid here at the moment?' Was she really unhappy and if so, why? From all accounts Godfrey was a kind and loving husband: he had provided April with a beautiful home and every conceivable luxury. She was living on a wonderful tropical island which appeared to have everything, from banana groves to blue lagoons. And sunshine.

Lovely, golden sunshine! (The thought of it was an almost irresistible temptation. Fancy not having to squelch to work through rain-drenched streets or stand at bus stops in a biting wind! Fancy spending the whole of November, that grey, chill and cheerless month, on an island where fog was unknown and where even the seawater was warm!)

But . . .! Much as she would like a holiday, much as she longed to see April again, there was an even more important consideration than the financial one. She hated the thought of tearing up the tender roots that had found it so difficult to take a hold in London's stony ground. She loved her job and knew that she was good at it. She didn't want to throw it up! Then there was this flat . . . it really was rather a nice one. If she went, Ann would be forced to find someone else to share, and there wasn't much chance that she'd be able to come back because there really wasn't enough room for three. (It had been a frightful squeeze when April was with them, they'd kept falling over each other's feet.) How could she bear to return to London and face the prospect of finding a new job, a new flat and new friends?

Ann knew her well enough to guess something of what she was thinking. She said, with unexpected gentleness, ' April doesn't sound frightfully happy, I agree, Lin, but it's probably only a passing phase. If you don't want to go to Tobago I don't see why you should have a guilty conscience about refusing.' Perhaps, she thought, it was merely that April was missing Lin more than she had expected to. After all, they had been as close as sisters for nearly seven years, and though she'd always suspected that April didn't really care two hoots about Lin, maybe in that one instance she had done her an injustice.

Lin looked at the letter again. ' I simply don't know what to do!' she broke out. She began coughing again and Ann's lips tightened.

' You're neglecting that cough, Lin. It's silly. You've had it far too long.'

' I know. I'm going to go and see the doctor tomorrow,' Lin said absently. She put her hand to her head, which was thumping worse than ever. ' You haven't got such a thing as an aspirin, have you, Ann? I've got a simply frightful headache, I've had it all day.'

' Well, worrying won't help it! Not that you've got anything to worry about, stupid! Just take a leaf out of April's book and do exactly what you want to do, whatever that may be,' Ann told her, disappearing kitchenwards to fetch both aspirins and the (overdone) Crépes Bon Viveur. In one way, she thought, it might be a good thing if Lin decided to accept April's invitation. She needed a holiday badly: she was beginning to look really ill. London had never suited her from the beginning: she was the sort of person who really only thrived in fresh country air.

Despite Ann's advice to sleep on it, Lin lay awake most of the night thinking about April's letter. It was all very well Ann telling her to do what she wanted to do, she thought ruefully, when for the life of her she simply couldn't make up her mind what that was! But of course Ann was wrong, anyway. What was important was whether April really needed her. If she did then nothing else mattered, and surely Aunt Bea would have felt that her legacy was being put to good use! Again and again her thoughts returned to those revealing phrases in April's letter—' Things are rather horrid here at the moment ' and ' Please don't let me down '—and long before she fell asleep she knew that there was only one thing for her to do. She would have to see for herself what was causing April's unrest. She owed it to Aunt Bea to do that much.

It was her doctor, the next day, who made her feel that she had made what was perhaps a lucky decision. When she visited his surgery she found rather to her surprise that he didn't dismiss her with a breezy remark and a bottle of tonic. Instead, he looked grave as he examined her and questioned her closely. Then he gave her a short, sharp warning. She was very run down, he told her, and if she was not careful she might find herself in real trouble before the end of the winter.

' I had a feeling he was getting ready to sign my death certificate!' she told Ann ruefully on her return from the surgery. ' I'm sure he'd think that a trip to the Caribbean would be the best medicine he could prescribe!' She hesitated. ' I—I've made up my mind, Ann. I'm going.'

' I thought you would,' Ann rejoined drily. ' At least I suppose I can be thankful that it appears to be for your own good as well as for April's!'

Lin laughed, but sobered again almost instantly.

' Ann, what will you do? You can't possibly afford to keep this flat on by yourself! What will you do—find somebody else to share with you?'

Ann coloured suddenly. For once she looked almost shy. 'I haven't had a chance to tell you yet! Charles and I had lunch together today and he asked me to marry him. He's been offered a job up North and says I've become so much a part of the scenery that he doesn't want to leave me behind!'

Lin's face blazed with delight. 'Ann! You and Charles? Oh, that's marvellous! I hoped it would happen!' She liked Charles Grainger immensely. He was an architect, rather quiet and shy but with a very attractive personality. Ann had known him for years, but it was only recently that their friendship had seemed to be deepening into something else.

Ann laughed. 'So did I!' she confessed. 'He's nice, isn't he? I'm glad—' She stopped short. She had nearly said, 'I'm glad I managed to keep him out of April's clutches.'

Lin had not noticed. She was too busy bombarding her with eager questions. 'Isn't it lucky that it's happened now? Where will you get married? You'll have a white wedding, won't you?'

'No fear!' Ann said inelegantly. 'The less fuss the better! If you want white veils and orange blossom you'll have to wait until it's your turn, my dear. You'd better see if you can find yourself a dreamboat in Tobago!'

'No, thanks!' Lin sounded genuinely indignant. Then she added, with a somewhat rueful little laugh, 'Anyway, you forget that April has got all the man-appeal in our family!'

That wasn't exactly true, Ann thought. Of course, April *was* a raving beauty, with her lovely blonde hair and wonderful figure, but Lin was pretty, too, with her brown eyes and fair hair which she wore clubbed in a fringe across her forehead, then falling straight and silky on to her shoulders. She could have plenty of boy-friends if she wanted, but she just wasn't interested. Not since Nicholas.

The thought of Nicholas still made Ann go hot with anger. Lin had met him soon after her arrival in London, and they had been firm friends until one evening Nicholas had called at the flat. He had met April and that was that, because she simply couldn't bear to see a personable young man taking an interest in any other female but herself. She had gone all out to attract Nicholas and had succeeded only too easily. Lin hadn't even put up a fight. Just as during their childhood she had always surrendered to April any toy or book that had happened to take her cousin's capricious fancy, so she now surrendered whatever claim she had to Nicholas. Of course it hadn't lasted, April's affairs never did, but Nicholas disappeared out of their lives for ever. Lin had never shown any resentment, but Ann suspected that the incident had left its scars and that it would be a long time before they healed completely.

She said now, lightly, 'Well, I imagine you'll lead a gay life in Tobago. Parties day and night.' She looked a little dubiously at Lin as she spoke. Lin didn't really like parties much—and certainly not April's kind.

'April can't spend all her time at parties,' Lin protested. 'There's the little girl, remember— Amanda. Somebody has to look after her.'

'And I bet it isn't April,' Ann thought grimly. April had precious little maternal instinct and what she had she wasn't likely to expend on someone else's child. Even her stepdaughter.

However, all she said was, 'I wonder if April is having a baby and that's what she means when she says that things are rather horrid at the moment?'

She spoke half jokingly, but Lin's eyes widened. That explanation had never even crossed her mind. She said naively, 'But a baby wouldn't be horrid, Ann!'

'Not to most people,' Ann agreed, looking amused. 'But April . . .' She shrugged.

Lin's face was sober. Could Ann be right? It didn't seem terribly likely, there was nothing complicated about a baby and surely no reason why April shouldn't have said she was expecting one. But it certainly seemed as though there was some kind of serpent in April's Eden. There had been a definite thread of dissatisfaction running through all her letters lately, though Lin had tried hard to persuade herself otherwise.

She sighed. Contrary to Ann's suppositions, she was not entirely blind where April was concerned, though loyally she still attempted to find excuses for her wild ways. She had hoped so much that April's marriage would be happy, and that she would settle down at last!

'What she needs is an anchor,' Aunt Bea had said before she died. 'Promise me you'll look after her when I've gone, Lin?' Lin had promised, and had kept her word. It was but a small return, she'd felt, for all that Aunt Bea had done for her, and in any case she was genuinely fond of her gay and lovely cousin. If only she weren't so—well, so wilful and headstrong! She found herself hoping, desperately, that whatever clouds there were on April's horizon would soon disperse, and that after all she would find nothing in Tobago to justify that faint prickling of foreboding which persisted despite all her attempts to shake it off.

CHAPTER II

Two weeks later Lin sat peering eagerly out of the window of the aircraft in which she was completing the last, and shortest, stage of her ten-hour journey from England to Tobago. A few more minutes and they would be landing. Already she could see, growing on the horizon, a fairy-tale island, with emerald-blue sea all around it and the rays of the setting sun flashing gold on to the wooded mountains. Silver beaches, coral reefs, green palm groves and exotic foliage . . . it all looked, she thought with a little shiver of excitement, almost too beautiful to be true.

Surreptitiously she pinched herself. She'd been doing that at intervals ever since she had left the grey cheerlessness of London Airport early that morning, but this time she pinched herself harder than she'd intended. Her involuntary ' Ouch! ' certainly proved she wasn't dreaming, but it also sounded embarrassingly loud. She looked round, wondering if anyone had heard her, and encountered a comprehensive glance from the tall, broad-shouldered man sitting next to her. His expression was nothing if not sardonic: Lin was left in no doubt that he had seen her childish action and that he was faintly amused. She coloured vividly. She'd amused him before, when shortly after taking off from Trinidad's Piarco Airport they had met an unexpected pocket of air and her face had betrayed her belief that they were headed for utter disaster. Not that he'd spoken, he was much too aloof for that, but there had been a mocking glint in his rather hard grey eyes. He looked tough and arrogant, Lin thought suddenly, and for some obscure reason found herself disliking him intensely. She'd been trying so hard to appear as much-travelled and as blasé as everyone else seemed to be, and the knowledge that he, at least, realized the truth was oddly disconcerting.

As if reading her thoughts he said unexpectedly, ' Your first visit to Tobago, I take it?' There was an inflection in his deep voice which she ascribed to superciliousness and it only added to her confusion.

' Why, yes. It looks simply marvellous . . . the most fabulous place I've ever seen . . .' She stopped abruptly, realizing in dismay that she must sound like a gushing schoolgirl. Her voice was the silly, nervous voice of someone ill at ease, and that was ridiculous, when she'd never seen this man before and was most unlikely ever to see him again once they'd landed in Tobago!

He said drily, ' You can spare me the adjectives. I've heard most of them before.'

He began fastening his seat belt as he spoke and Lin, suddenly realizing that they were coming in to land, did likewise. Her indignation at his curt rejoinder was swamped by a sudden wave of excited anticipation. At last she would see April again . . . her home, her husband and little stepdaughter!

Throughout the journey the same few anxious questions had chased themselves round and round in her head . . . questions about April, about Godfrey, about their life together on Tobago, and very soon now she would know the answers.

They landed, and Lin was one of the first to leave the plane, brushing past the grey-eyed man with a curt ' Excuse me, please!' Her excitement was now at fever-pitch. She forgot that, though the journey had been somewhat boring in its utter uneventfulness, she was feeling limp and exhausted and also slightly sick. There were pins and needles in her nerves, but the warm velvety air touched her cheeks like a kind of benediction as her eyes searched eagerly for April.

She wasn't there.

For a moment Lin felt almost crushed by a sickening sense of disappointment. April had promised faithfully to meet her! Of course, it might be that she was just a little late, punctuality never had been one of her virtues, but . . . oh, surely on this one occasion she might have tried to be on time!

The huge orange-red globe of the sun vanished, and the swift dusk fell. People came and went, but she stood forlornly by the barrier, looking piteously around her, for nearly fifteen minutes before she at last began to face up to the fact that April wasn't coming. Perhaps because she was so desperately tired and disappointed, she was suddenly all to pieces. She was all alone, thousands of miles away from home, in a strange island where people spoke English but with such a strange accent that it almost seemed that she had arrived in a foreign country rather than a Commonwealth one! Her throat swelled with the tears she would not shed, and despite the heat her hands felt cold and clammy. She tried to make up her mind what to do, but it seemed as though it was numbed by the awful fear that something had happened to April on the way to the airport.

'Miss Grierson?' In her preoccupation she had not noticed the tall, bronzed man approaching her, and she looked up with a start of surprise as she heard her name. Her first impression was that this was the most handsome man she had ever seen. He had an air of intense virility combined with sophistication, and the whole added up to the sort of powerful, careless charm which even at that moment she realized could be quite devastating.

'Why, yes, but . . .'

He smiled a little at her confusion, and the smile was reflected in his dark eyes.

'My name is Luis Cortes. I am a friend of your cousin's. She is unfortunately indisposed and is unable to meet you as she promised. She has asked me to take her place and to escort you to Buonaventura.' His voice was low-pitched and pleasant, but something about his meticulous English made Lin realize that to him, in fact, it was a foreign tongue.

'April's ill? What's the matter?' she asked sharply.

'Oh, it is nothing,' Luis Cortes assured her quickly. 'Only a touch of migraine. But she did not feel up to the drive to the airport, and I was only too delighted to have the pleasure of meeting you so soon. I have heard a lot about you.'

The warmth in his voice was nothing if not flattering, but Lin was too tired and overwrought to notice it. She swayed slightly, and Luis Cortes' smile changed to an expression of concern as he noticed her extreme pallor.

'Was it a rough flight? You also are not feeling well?'

Lin managed an unsteady laugh. 'It's all right. I'm just a little tired, I think. Is—is it far to Buonaventura?'

'Some fifteen miles, I'm afraid.' He hesitated momentarily. 'Look, I was going to ask you whether you minded if I drove you into Scarborough first? I promised to contact an old friend who's staying at an hotel there and I don't like the idea of just not turning up. I could buy you a drink at the same time—you look as though you could do with a pick-me-up.'

Lin's heart sank. All she really wanted to do was to get to Buonaventura as quickly as possible, but it was impossible to do anything but acquiesce.

If Luis Cortes noticed her lack of enthusiasm he gave no sign of it. 'By the way, I must apologize for my late arrival,' he said, as cupping her elbow in his hand he piloted her to his car, a black Sunbeam Alpine. 'I found I had a flat tyre and I had to stop to change it.'

'I'm afraid I'm being an awful nuisance——'

'Not at all.' Luis opened the car door for Lin as he spoke and she sank into the passenger seat with a sigh of relief. It was nice of Luis to do all this for a girl he'd never even met before, she thought with a rush of gratitude. April certainly seemed to have made some good friends.

'Have you known April long?' The question almost asked itself.

'Only a few weeks. I have but recently returned to Tobago from the States, you understand. I was born and bred on the island, but a few years ago I left to seek my fortune in America.'

He seemed to have found it, Lin thought. This car wasn't a poor man's car. Come to that, nearly everything about Luis Cortes proclaimed a large bank balance. It almost amounted to ostentation, but she dismissed the idea the moment it entered her head. After all, if he had made a lot of money there was no earthly reason why he shouldn't spend it!

Luis drove fast and well—almost too fast for Lin, who found the unfamiliar scenery reduced to a blur of ever-changing contours and mysterious violet shadows. It was a cloudless night and though the moon had not yet risen the road was not really dark. Ahead of them she could see the lights that spangled the streets of Scarborough, Tobago's tiny capital, and as they entered the town she caught tantalizing glimpses of diminutive houses with louvred windows and doors and lacy fretwork, wide, clean streets and open-fronted shops, and overlooking the bay the old Fort King George. It seemed to be very much a country town and she was glad of that, for it fitted in with her preconception of the island as a kind of unspoilt Paradise.

Luis kept up a running commentary as he drove, and since his remarks were spiced with gaiety and humour Lin found herself enjoying his company far more than she had expected. By the time they had reached a blaze of golden neon that proclaimed ' The Half Moon Hotel ' and Luis had turned the car into a short drive, lined with bushes of bougainvillea, she was feeling much more relaxed and a little colour had returned to her cheeks.

The Half Moon Hotel was a white, lowslung building made of coral stone. Luis pulled into a parking place and Lin followed him into a large bamboo bar, furnished with grass mats and orange and green wickerwork. It opened on one side to a swimming pool and on another to a patio, where small tables were dotted about under palm trees. From a gaudily dressed trio, seated at the end of a small deserted cement dance floor, came the throb and twang of calypso music.

The bar was crowded. Luis bought Lin a drink without first enquiring what she wanted: it was a sparkling amber liquid in a tall, frosted glass and it looked cool and refreshing.

' This will do you the world of good,' Luis said, smiling as he handed her the glass. ' It is a local speciality. And now, if you will excuse me for a moment, I must see if I can find Henry.'

Lin was left alone to sip her drink. For all its innocuous appearance it burned the back of her throat and for a moment she hesitated. Because she had felt slightly sick on the plane she had had nothing to eat all day and she remembered that it was supposed to be unwise to drink alcohol on an empty stomach. Then she shrugged. Whatever this concoction was there was no doubt about its efficacy as a pick-me-up. Her tiredness was evaporating

27

already. One drink couldn't hurt her, she decided, but she wouldn't let Luis buy her any more.

He seemed to be a long time coming back. She let her glance wander round the bar, which was filled mostly by coloured people, then almost spilt her drink. She was looking straight into the hard grey eyes of the man who had sat beside her on the flight from Trinidad and who was now seated, alone, at a small table not three or four yards away from her. There was a flicker of—what? surprise?—in his eyes as he met her look, then he turned his head deliberately away. Lin, who had started to give him a small, wavering smile of recognition, felt the colour flood into her cheeks. What on earth did he think— that she was trying to pick him up? Hot with indignation, she finished her drink and stood up. She'd go and wait for Luis on the patio, as far away from that abominable creature as she possibly could!

She took two steps, then to her horror found herself swaying forwards. She had the oddest sensation of being hot and cold at once, there was a roaring in her ears, and the whole room seemed to be revolving round her at top speed.

Instinctively she closed her eyes, and the next moment she felt a vice-like grip on her arm and somebody was steering her through the crowded bar out on to the patio. The next few moments were a blur, but when she again opened her eyes it was to find that she was sitting in a chair under one of the green palm trees and the grey-eyed man was bending over her, his expression grim.

' Better?' he asked peremptorily.

She didn't answer. She felt as though her humilia-

28

tion was complete. She had never been so close to fainting before in her whole life, and the memory of that awful roaring dizziness still frightened her. She put an unsteady hand up to her eyes. The patio still swam around her, a little too bright and a little out of focus.

She realized that the grey-eyed man was waiting for her to speak, but when her voice came it was only a thin thread. 'Yes. I'm sorry.'

He regarded her frowningly. 'Are you in the habit of fainting all over the place?'

'Oh!' Lin gasped, then rallied. She said indignantly, 'Certainly not! It—I think it must have been the drink I had. I—I haven't had anything to eat all day.'

'And you drank a rum punch on top of an empty stomach?' The man gave a short laugh. 'You were simply asking for trouble, weren't you?'

Oh, where was Luis? Lin longed to get up and walk away, but though her head had cleared her legs still felt a bit like cottonwool and she wasn't quite sure whether they would support her. She said, and in spite of herself her voice trembled a little, 'I suppose I was.'

'Where is Cortes?' The question came abruptly, so abruptly that Lin jumped and stared. How did he know who she was with? Oh, of course—he must have seen them enter the bar together! Was he a friend of Luis'? Not necessarily—on an island this size probably everyone knew everyone else.

She said stiffly, 'He'll be back in a moment. He's taking me to my cousin's home—Buonaventura. I'm going to stay with her for a few weeks.'

She was totally unprepared for the effect of her words. For once he looked thoroughly taken aback.

' Buonaventura? Do you mean—is April Selby your cousin?' The words rapped out.

' Why, yes . . .'

' Then where the devil is she? And what the hell are you doing here with Cortes—alone?' There was no doubt about it, it was anger that was blazing in the grey eyes now.

Lin had stiffened. The colour rushed into her face again as she retorted, with as much icy dignity as she could muster, ' Pardon me! I really can't see that it's any of your business!'

Her small chin was very much in evidence and there was an angry sparkle in her own eyes. How *dare* he cross-examine her, and in that tone of voice?

For a moment he stared down at her, then he said coldly, ' Perhaps I'd better introduce myself. I'm Ruel Saxon.' He saw from her blank expression that the name meant nothing to her and his lips tightened. ' I am Godfrey Selby's stepson. At present I am staying at Buonaventura.'

' *Stepson?*' Lin stared at him, her thoughts whirling. ' Oh, but you can't be . . . April's never said . . .' She stopped helplessly. April had never mentioned the existence of anyone called Ruel Saxon! She said flatly, ' I don't believe you!'

' April's never told you about me?' There was a gleam of something that might have been mockery in Ruel Saxon's eyes. ' I suppose I should be mortified that she didn't consider me worthy of mention! Nonetheless, I assure you that I am speaking the truth.'

Lin put her hand to her head. 'Amanda . . .'

'Is my half-sister. My mother was married twice. I am the son of her first marriage,' Ruel said coolly. He saw by her expression that she was convinced, and his tone changed.

'My identity having been established, will you now please answer my first question? Where *is* April?'

Lin swallowed. To her enormous surprise she heard herself saying meekly, 'She isn't well. That's why she asked Luis to meet me.'

At that moment she felt, rather than saw, Ruel stiffen beside her. Turning her head, she saw Luis walking across the patio towards them and even at that distance she noticed that for the first time his handsome face was unsmiling.

Hideously embarrassed, she jumped up. 'Have you been looking for me?' Her voice sounded quite unlike her own, much too hard and brittle. 'I wanted some fresh air—— '

Luis did not let her finish. 'I'm sorry I've been so long. My friend was very late.'

He spoke to her, but he looked at Ruel, and as the eyes of the two men met it was like the clash of steel. Lin thought in horror: 'They hate each other . . .' and then Ruel was speaking.

'I've just introduced myself, Cortes. I understand Mrs Selby has asked you to escort her cousin to Buonaventura, but there's no need to put yourself out. I'm going home myself and I may as well take her along with me.'

He spoke brusquely, and with a calm assumption of authority that made Lin gasp. 'Luis might be a

—a porter and I might be a parcel or a piece of luggage that no one particularly wants!' she thought indignantly, and looked at Luis. Oh, surely he wasn't going to let Ruel Saxon get away with that!

She knew from the way Luis' hands were clenched at his sides that he was making a tremendous effort to control his temper. Tight-lipped, he said, ' I am not putting myself out. I have already assured Miss Grierson that it will be a pleasure to escort her to Buonaventura.'

' Then it's a pleasure I'm afraid you'll have to forgo,' Ruel said coolly. ' I feel sure, don't you, that it is more appropriate that Mrs Selby's cousin should be welcomed to Buonaventura by a member of the family?' He paused, and there was an odd gleam in his eyes as he added, ' After all, I very much doubt whether Mrs Selby would have solicited your services had she known that I was available.'

There was something here that Lin did not understand. Evidently Luis did, for he flushed darkly. Lin, confused and angry, longed to shout out, ' I don't want to go with you! I want to go with Luis!' but something kept her silent. She looked imploringly at Luis, and was momentarily startled by the ugly expression on his face.

Then it had gone. They were beginning to attract attention: several people were already looking curiously in their direction and it was probably because of this, Lin thought, that Luis suddenly surrendered. ' As you will.' He took Lin's hand, ignoring Ruel, smiled down into her anxious eyes. ' I hope we'll meet again, Miss Grierson. I am only sorry that our acquaintanceship on this occasion has been so brief.'

'So am I. Thank you very much for being so kind and helpful,' Lin said, very clearly and distinctly. She felt extremely sorry for Luis: he had been put in an invidious position and had doubtless given way to Ruel Saxon merely because the prospect of a brawl in a public place was totally unwelcome! Ruel Saxon looked capable of anything, she thought angrily.

'Have her luggage transferred from your car to mine, won't you?' Ruel said lazily. 'Straightaway, if you don't mind. I'm leaving in a moment.'

Lin held her breath, but Luis merely nodded. She watched him walk away, with the easy careless grace that was so much a part of him, and then turned angrily towards Ruel, who was regarding her with a kind of grim amusement.

'Unless you want another drink, Miss Grierson— and I don't advise it—we'll go. I'm sure you're longing to see your cousin.'

Lin looked him straight in the eyes. 'Did you have to be so beastly rude to him?' she asked hotly. 'He was only being kind!'

Ruel raised his brows. 'Do I detect a note of chagrin?' he asked mockingly. 'Can it possibly be that you prefer Luis Cortes' company to my own?'

'Since you ask me—yes!' Lin flashed.

Ruel did not appear to be in the least put out. 'Dear, dear! What an impressionable young woman you seem to be!' he said lazily. 'I remember thinking so on the plane.'

Lin bit back the scathing retort that trembled on her lips. Argument would obviously be useless. There was some old enmity between Luis Cortes and this man, of that she was certain, but whatever it was it did not really concern her. She had merely been caught in the cross-currents. 'Shall we go?'

'By all means.'

They walked to his car in silence. The black Sunbeam Alpine had already gone.

'Hop in.' Ruel held the door open for her and Lin, still smarting, did as she was told. Ten minutes later the town of Scarborough lay behind them, and with the moon riding high overhead, and the stars twinkling against the sable backcloth of the sky, they were heading towards a distant mountain range clothed in dense woods.

Ruel drove the powerful car, a Chevrolet, at a steady fast pace along the winding road with its hidden corners and bends. Sixty miles an hour. His hands on the wheel were strong and capable, with square, well-kept nails. His profile was forbidding: looking at him covertly from beneath her gold-tipped lashes Lin found herself suppressing an almost hysterical desire to giggle. 'Poor April!' she thought. 'Fancy having such a high-handed stepson!' Why had she never mentioned him? she wondered. It was odd, when she'd written such volumes about everything else. It might be that he was just a shadowy figure in the background, but somehow that explanation seemed unlikely. Ruel Saxon didn't strike her as the sort of man who'd be content with a background role.

'Are you staying long in Tobago?' The question took her by surprise. It was the first time Ruel had spoken since they had left the hotel, and she had found it impossible not to contrast this silent journey with the gaiety of the drive from the airport to Scarborough. He could scarcely have made it clearer that he wasn't enjoying her company, she thought ruefully. Well, she hadn't invited herself!

'I—I don't know. I'll stay as long as April wants me to, I suppose, if—if your stepfather doesn't mind.'

'Godfrey? Why should he mind? Anything that April does is all right with him,' Ruel said in a voice that was devoid of expression. 'Anyway, he's away at the moment. In New York.'

'Oh!' Lin digested that piece of news in silence. She was rather relieved that Godfrey was still away. It would be lovely to have April to herself . . . or would that, in fact, be the case? Where did Ruel fit into Buonaventura? She felt the first stirrings of curiosity regarding him and tried, for the first time, to obtain an objective picture that was not coloured by the antagonism she could not help feeling. He was, she judged, in his early thirties . . . not handsome, too rough-hewn for that, but completely male. Now that the angry lines of his brow and mouth had been smoothed away he had instead a withdrawn and brooding look: he was not, she thought suddenly, a happy man.

On impulse she said, 'You must have been very surprised when your stepfather married my cousin.'

For a moment he did not answer. Then in the same expressionless voice he had used before he said, 'If you are seeking information from me I'm afraid you'll be unlucky. I detest gossip.'

Lin almost choked. This wretched man had the knack of making her feel a perfect fool! She hadn't had the slightest intention of gossiping! She sat, tight-lipped, looking out of the window. She wouldn't say another word!

The scenery was wilder now and looked, to Lin's English eyes, strangely unreal. They had long ago left the windward road, with its spectacular views of the sea, scintillating in the moonlight, and the forested hills and deep valleys reminded her of a tropical Switzerland. One could live here for a thousand years, she thought, and find some fresh beauty every day.

'Buonaventura,' Ruel said suddenly, and swung the car into a long drive lined with hibiscus and bushes of bougainvillea. The house came into view, and Lin could not suppress an exclamation of delight. It was a big Georgian country mansion with a handsome, white-pillared portico, and it might, when new, have been hideous. Now, however, it had mellowed with age and achieved with the dignity of maturity a kind of beauty. Flowering creepers broke the starkness of the stone, and it was surrounded by a beautiful garden.

Ruel stopped the car at the bottom of a sweep of steps which led to the open front door and Lin got out, glad to stretch her legs after the long drive. There was the sound of excited barking, and two cocker spaniels hurled themselves down the steps to grovel at Ruel's feet, writhing in a frenzy of welcome. Ruel bent down to caress their silky heads just as April appeared in the doorway, slender and fragile in white dress, her golden hair gleaming in the light that streamed from behind her. She started to run down the steps, but halfway she suddenly stood stock-still, an almost comical expression of surprise and dismay on her face as Ruel, straightening, gave her a casual salute.

' *Ruel!* I thought you were in Trinidad! '

Ruel leant against the side of the car and stuck his hands in his pockets. Then he said, in his slow drawl, ' But as you see, April dear, I have now returned.'

The air was suddenly electric. Lin, looking from one to the other, realized with a sudden wave of shocked indignation that April was actually frightened.

CHAPTER III

It was Ruel who broke the tension.

' Well, aren't you going to welcome your cousin?' he enquired pleasantly, and April flushed scarlet, quickly recovering her self-possession.

' Of course. Hello, Lin, lovely to see you again. Had a pleasant journey?' She proffered one soft, scented cheek for Lin's kiss, then stood back to give her cousin a quick critical appraisal. It seemed to Lin that she was making a conscious effort to ignore the tall brooding figure behind them. ' Goodness, you do look peaked! Haven't you been well?'

' I'm all right, thanks. Is your migraine better?'

' My—? Oh, yes!' April gave a brittle little laugh. ' Luis did meet you at the airport, then? How did you manage to join forces with Ruel?' Her voice was uneasy, almost defiant, Lin thought.

Ruel answered for her. ' We met at the Half

37

Moon Hotel, where your friend Cortes had seen fit to deposit her,' he said coolly. 'It occurred to me that a change of escort might be—desirable.'

April's eyes flashed. 'Minding my business as usual, Ruel?' Temper flicked suddenly, patently, through the words like a whip. Lin saw Ruel's face harden, and his eyes were ice-cold as he answered her.

'I've told you before, April. What you do is very much my business. It would be as well if you remember that.'

He nodded curtly in Lin's direction as he walked away, the dogs yapping joyously at his heels.

April turned to Lin. She was almost crying with anger. 'Oh, God, that *insufferable* man! He makes me sick! Lin, if you only *knew* what I've had to put up with! I hate him! I despise him!'

She did not bother to lower her voice and her words must have been clearly audible, not only to Ruel's retreating figure but also to the two dusky-skinned servants who had appeared in the doorway.

Lin slipped her arm through her cousin's, automatically reverting to her familiar role of comforter, protector and adviser. April probably had every justification for her almost hysterical outburst—already Lin had no doubts on *that* score—but Ruel was, after all, Godfrey Selby's stepson and it was surely imprudent of April to give vent to her outraged feelings in public.

'April, don't make a scene! Tell me when we're alone! Can't we go inside? I'm longing to see your home!'

For a moment Lin thought that April was going

38

to shake off her restraining hand, then the rigidity went out of her slender figure and she forced a laugh. Like Lin she had become aware of the presence of the servants, who were hurrying down the steps to unload the luggage from the car.

' Oh, all right! I'll show you your bedroom: you'll have time for a shower before dinner if you hurry. You can see the rest of the house later.' She paused and added lightly, ' You'll find it all a bit different from that poky little cottage you liked so much or that dreadful flat at Maida Vale!'

She didn't need to be warned about the difference, Lin thought wryly as April escorted her to a bedroom that was more lovely and more luxurious than anything she had ever imagined in her whole life. She looked round, wide-eyed, at the exquisite fittings and furnishings, but April gave her no chance to comment.

' Now tell me every single thing that happened! How on earth did Ruel know who you were? What did he say to Luis?' It was obvious that she was labouring under such a strong sense of grievance that for the moment she could think of nothing else.

Now that they were alone Lin answered her readily, her indignation matching April's own. It was not only that she was still furious at the way in which Ruel had more or less abducted her without the slightest regard for anyone's wishes but his own. It was also that she could not forget that frightened expression on her cousin's lovely face when she had first caught sight of Ruel. The man was obviously an out-and-out bully! she thought angrily.

April's chagrin when Lin reached the end of her

story was apparent.

'Of course Ruel would do anything he possibly could to upset me!' she said bitterly. 'It's been like that from the very beginning!'

Lin seized her chance. 'Why have you never mentioned him in your letters? I just didn't believe it when he said he was Godfrey Selby's stepson!'

April gave a mirthless laugh. 'I didn't know about him myself until after I'd married Godfrey. I suppose the silly man thought I wouldn't much care for a stepson eight years older than myself, so he kept it dark! Not that it would have mattered— then. Ruel doesn't live here, you see. He's practically a hermit—he's buried himself on some queer little island which isn't even on the map and he paints or something, though I've never seen any of his work.'

'Oh!' Lin looked at her, startled and in spite of herself a little intrigued. No wonder Ruel Saxon was so lacking in social graces, if he normally led the life of a recluse! 'Why did he come back?'

April snapped open a gold cigarette case and lit a cigarette before answering 'Oh, he comes home fairly frequently, principally to see Mandy, I think. But this time Godfrey asked him to come. There's some kind of lawsuit dragging on in New York—I don't quite know what it's all about, it's too involved, but if things go against him Godfrey stands to lose quite a lot of money. He decided in the end that he ought to be on the spot, so he asked Ruel to come and look after the plantations while he hobnobs with his lawyers in New York' She flung herself down on a rose-pink divan, her expression still stormy. 'The trouble is that Ruel thinks he's entitled to run me as well as the silly old plantations! He's absolutely furious because Godfrey's married again, of course. Jealousy, I suppose . . . he's afraid that I'm going to deprive him of his rights! Not that he's got any, really . . . he isn't Godfrey's own son, after all.'

April's soft red lips suddenly trembled. 'I tried to be nice to him at first, I did really, Lin! But you heard the way he spoke to me! He's been like that all the time. I know he'd like nothing better than to make trouble between Godfrey and me . . . he *spies* on me, Lin! He puts the worst possible construction on everything I do, and I'm sure he's storing it all up to tell Godfrey! He criticizes what I say, what I do, the money I spend, the friends I make . . . I can't do *anything* right!'

'April!' Lin stared at her aghast. 'How beastly for you! Is that what you meant when you said that things were rather horrid here at the moment?'

'Yes, of course.' April's blue eyes were wide and wistful. 'Lin, it isn't my fault if I like parties and gay and amusing people, is it? Ruel seems to think I should sit at home and—and sew samplers or something while Godfrey isn't here! But Godfrey wouldn't want me to be lonely, he likes me to have fun! I'm sure he wouldn't mind if I went dancing with Luis!'

'Perhaps Ruel is worried about your reputation,' Lin suggested after a moment, remembering Luis' dark good looks and careless charm. Together, he and April would form a striking combination. If they had been seeing a lot of each other during

Godfrey's absence . . .

' What?'   April stared at her, then gave an impatient laugh.   ' Oh, really, Lin!   This isn't the
depths of Warwickshire, thank heaven!'

Lin said slowly, ' But Ruel doesn't like Luis,
does he?   Do you know why?'

April blew out a cloud of smoke.   ' Oh, yes!   It's
quite a long story and needless to say it doesn't
rebound to Ruel's credit!'   She got up and stubbed
out her cigarette with unnecessary violence before
turning again to Lin.   ' Three or four years ago Luis
was employed here at Buonaventura.   He was clever
and ambitious and he had good prospects.   He and
Ruel were on quite friendly terms in those days,
until they had a simply frightful row over some
French girl who had come to live near here.   Her
father was an artist or something, I think.   Anyway,
Ruel fell head over heels in love with her, but she
preferred Luis—well, who wouldn't?   Ruel was a
rotten loser: he got Luis the sack on some pretext
or other and then he saw to it that nobody else on
the island would employ him.   To cap it all there
was the most frightful accident and the girl was
drowned.   Of course Luis had absolutely nothing
at all to do with it, but Ruel went berserk, insisted
that he was entirely to blame and practically had him
drummed out of the island.   There was nothing
much poor Luis could do about it—he'd got no
money, no job and no important friends to take his
part.'

She smiled crookedly in acknowledgement of Lin's
horrified exclamation.   ' Of course the situation is
quite different now.   Luis made a lot of money in the

States, so he's very much persona grata. He doesn't bear any grudges, either, he's quite willing to let bygones be bygones, but that isn't dear Ruel's way. There's nothing he can do to harm Luis now, but he's made it perfectly plain that as far as he's concerned he's still the penniless nobody who had the effrontery to steal the young master's girl-friend! He can't bear it because *I* like him—and of course it makes him furious every time Luis comes anywhere near his beloved Buonaventura!'

'I . . . see,' Lin said, after a long pause. Yes, she could quite believe that someone as arrogant as Ruel Saxon appeared to be would find it impossible ever to forgive anything which had struck a blow at his pride. Yet at the same time she had a fleeting remembrance of the deep unhappiness of Ruel's lean, sunburnt face. Presumably it had been because of that tragic little French girl that he had left Buonaventura and 'buried' himself on some remote little island. Had he loved her so much that even now he could not forget her?

April gave her a quick look. 'Did you like Luis, Lin?'

'I thought he was charming,' Lin told her.

April seemed pleased. 'He is, isn't he? He dances divinely, too, and he's terrific fun to be with. Things really hum when Luis is around!'

Lin was silent. Surely April had spoken with rather too much enthusiasm for a married woman? Oh, but of course she'd always had a bevy of admirers—she was so used to breathing the incense of male attention that she'd be lost without it. She didn't really mean any harm. In spite of herself she thought of Nicholas. She always tried not to . . . his defection had hurt her so badly, especially as she had known in her heart of hearts that April wasn't really interested in him save as another conquest . . . and now she winced hastily away from the memory of his laughing brown eyes and infectious smile. Nicholas belonged to the past. What mattered now was the future—April's future.

She said, rather uneasily, 'April, are you quite sure Godfrey wouldn't mind your seeing Luis?'

April's lovely face hardened. 'If he isn't prepared to amuse me himself he can hardly blame me for seeking entertainment elsewhere! But you needn't worry, my little Puritan!'—with a swift amused look in Lin's direction. 'I don't do anything I shouldn't, whatever dear Ruel may suspect to the contrary!' She tossed back her long blonde hair. 'Incidentally, Lin, you'd better try to keep out of Ruel's way as much as you can. It's better if there isn't any more unpleasantness.'

'You may be quite sure I shall avoid him,' Lin said drily. 'Come to that, I can safely predict that he'll return the compliment! He doesn't like me any more than he likes you. He made that quite plain!'

'Oh, since that girl died he's turned into a complete mis—what is it you call somebody who can't bear women? I've forgotten.'

'Misogynist.'

'That's right. Well, that's what Ruel is. As hard as nails and as sour as crab apples.' She glanced at her small diamond wristwatch and jumped up. 'Heavens, it's nearly time for dinner! Do you

44

want a quick shower? There's the bathroom: you've got one to yourself.'

'What luxury!' Lin said, laughing, pleased to see that April was recovering something of her usual animation. That aggrieved, almost sullen air didn't suit her: Ruel Saxon must have got badly under her skin. It would be a good thing when Godfrey returned!

The bathroom was as luxuriously appointed as the bedroom and there was the same soft pink carpet on the floor. Lin grinned a little to herself. Several weeks at Buonaventura and she would be completely spoiled! At the cottage the bath had been an old-fashioned affair, little more than a tin tub, and the plumbing had been of such a dubious nature that a hot bath had always been acclaimed as a miracle. And at Maida Vale there had always been a queue for the bathroom, and woe betide her who occupied it for longer than ten minutes or took more than her fair share of the hot water!

When she went back into the bedroom April was still sitting on the bed. She watched critically while Lin rummaged in her suitcase for a blue Courtelle dress that she had bought before leaving home.

'You're much too thin, Lin . . . you need to put some flesh on those skinny bones! But that's quite a nice dress: where did you get it?'

'It was a present from Mr Heriot,' Lin told her airily.

April's eyebrows shot up. *What?*

'A leaving present,' Lin explained. 'He gave me a bonus of twenty-five pounds. Wasn't it nice of him? I spent it all on clothes so that I shouldn't disgrace you by appearing in rags!' She laughed reminiscently. 'It was rather fun, shopping for swimsuits and cottons while everyone else was rushing madly around looking for chunky sweaters and winter coats!'

April pulled a face. 'Don't remind me of the English climate! As for the bonus, I expect you'd earned it. Honestly, Lin, how you *stuck* that frightful job for so long I simply don't know! You were crazy to choose a secretarial career: I can't think of anything duller, except perhaps teaching!'

'I enjoyed it.' Lin zipped up the blue dress and began to brush her hair. 'And Mr Heriot was rather a dear to work for.'

'You always were easily satisfied.' April's face was suddenly sombre. 'I never was.'

Lin felt as though a cold finger had been laid on her heart. She laid the brush down and swung round to face her cousin. 'But you are now, April?' Her tone was almost pleading. 'Godfrey sounds so nice and he's been so good to you! And you've got the loveliest home: it's just like a dream come true!'

'Oh, the house isn't so bad,' April said grudgingly. 'But of course it's in completely the wrong part of the island. Tobago isn't much fun anyway. I wish we lived in Jamaica or Barbados: that's where the really smart set congregate! I get so fed up with nothing much to do, and Godfrey's such an old stick-in-the-mud!' She paused and added pettishly, 'I wanted him to take me with him to New York, but he wouldn't hear of it. Said I'd be too much of a distraction, if you please!'

'Well, he was probably right. You and a lawsuit

46

don't exactly mix!' Lin said, trying to hide her dismay. There was nothing in April's manner to suggest that she was an adoring wife! Was it possible that Ann was right—that April *had* married Godfrey Selby solely and simply for his money? But no, of course she wasn't—April was bored and lonely and so she was saying things she didn't really mean.

April scowled at her. 'Maybe not. But I can't say that *I* think much of his kindness, leaving me here with no one but his abominable stepchildren to keep me company!' she retorted.

Lin said slowly, 'You don't like Amanda either?'

April shrugged. 'You know I'm not keen on children. Besides, Mandy's a weird kid—not a bit pretty, and she won't let me buy her any decent clothes. She's been hopelessly spoilt, of course: Ruel and Godfrey have seen to that. She practically runs wild, I've given up trying to control her.'

She glanced at her watch again. 'Aren't you ready yet? Aunt Lou—that's the cook—has hysterics if she has to keep things hot.'

'I've only got to powder my nose.' Lin hesitated. 'Will—will Ruel be at dinner?'

'Most improbable! He's got his own small bungalow: he prefers to be independent, and that suits me down to the ground. The less I see of him the better,' April said, almost viciously. 'Actually I'd meant to ask Luis to stay to dinner, but of course dear Ruel has scotched that little plan!'

'Oh well, you can ask him another night,' Lin soothed her.

'Yes, but he's going to Jamaica tomorrow. He

47

won't be back for a day or two,' April said, and again the sullen air was much in evidence.

Lin looked round for her handbag, which contained both her powder and lipstick. Somebody had brought her suitcase up while she was having a shower, but a quick search revealed no trace of the brown leather bag which had been a parting gift from Ann.

'April, I can't find my bag!' Lin's voice was suddenly sharp with dismay. In that bag was everything she had of value—passport, return ticket and every penny she possessed.

April joined in the search. 'Well, it isn't here,' she said at last. 'You must have left it in the car, Lin.'

'I—I don't think I did. I don't believe I had it then.' Lin had been desperately ransacking her memory and her face had gone very white. She had been carrying the bag when she and Luis had entered the bamboo bar at the Half Moon Hotel: she distinctly recollected placing it in front of her on the small wicker table. Then there'd come that frightful roaring dizziness . . . and for the life of her she couldn't remember whether she had picked the bag up or not. She was almost sure she hadn't.

'For goodness' sake, Lin!' April sounded irritated. 'Are you trying to tell me you don't know *where* you've left it?'

'I—I think it may be at the Half Moon Hotel. Can—can I ring up to see if anyone's found it?'

'The phone's out of order, has been all day,' April said bleakly. She paused, then added, 'That's why Luis couldn't warn me about you and Ruel.'

' But surely there's a public telephone . . . ? '

' There isn't another phone for miles. It cost Godfrey a fortune to have one installed here.' She frowned at the sight of Lin's obvious distress. ' You probably *did* leave it in the car, idiot! I'll ask Joseph to check. If not—well, you'll just have to keep your fingers crossed and hope for the best. Why on earth weren't you more careful? '

Lin said nothing. Impossible to explain to April that she'd been so tired and overwrought that practically all her wits had deserted her! It was Ruel Saxon's fault, she told herself bitterly. She wasn't usually forgetful: if it hadn't been for him she would never have been so silly!

Joseph, a tall West Indian with very dark twinkling eyes and expressive hands, was detailed to search Ruel's car, but soon reported back that he had found nothing.

' Then I *must* have left it at the hotel! ' Lin tried unsuccessfully to hide her growing agitation. What would she do if the bag was not recovered? ' April, isn't there *any* way we can find out if they've got it? '

' Not tonight.' April spoke impatiently. ' Do be sensible, Lin! It's futile to worry. If they've got it they'll certainly hang on to it, and if they haven't . . . well, there's nothing much that anyone can do about that! But don't worry, the Tobagans are a pretty honest lot on the whole. It'll turn up.'

' I hope you're right.' Lin forced a smile, but her anxiety and apprehension did not lessen, and since April herself seemed somewhat distraite dinner was rather a silent meal. Neither did much justice to the menu—callalou soup, followed by enormous

49

steaks of grilled king-fish with tomato and lettuce salad, sweet potatoes and a bowl of rice.

Lin, glancing round the cool, airy room, with its big windows opening on to the terrace, its pale blue walls and white paint setting off to perfection the gilt of the Italian mirrors and the pale gold polished wood of the Swedish furniture, thought with an inexplicable shiver that despite its luxury the big house seemed strangely quiet and lonely . . . voice-less. It was hardly surprising that April craved for companionship!

' Where's Amanda—Mandy, I mean?' she asked suddenly. She realized that she had been waiting to hear the silence broken by a child's laugh or the sound of running footsteps. ' She's not in bed, is she?'

' Heavens, no! She goes to bed when she feels like it,' April said, giving another of those slight shrugs which seemed plainly to indicate that the matter was not really her responsibility. ' If she's discovered that Ruel is back she'll probably spend the night with him at the bungalow. She adores him, though goodness knows why!'

' But—April! Oughtn't you to find out for sure if she is there?' Lin demurred. She dared not say too much while April was in her present difficult mood, but she could not help feeling rather horrified by her cousin's casual attitude towards her small stepdaughter.

April shot her a look that was half amused, half resentful. ' My dear coz, you needn't worry about Mandy! She's quite capable of looking after her-self.' Then, as Lin still looked faintly dubious, she added, ' Aunt Lou keeps a weather eye on her. You may be quite sure that if anything was wrong she'd soon give the alarm! Half the island would know within five minutes!'

' Don't you have anything to do with Mandy at all?' Too late Lin realized that the question held a definite hint of criticism and bit her lip. April was already on edge and that kind of tactless remark was hardly likely to improve matters.

' My dear Lin, we do have a bevy of servants!' April's voice was cold. ' Besides, Mandy wouldn't thank me for trying to mother her! She's too much like Ruel for that—completely self-sufficient.' She rose to her feet. ' We'll have coffee in the drawing room, shall we?'

The drawing room had the kind of graceful elegance that can only be produced by money and good taste. Realizing that she was expected to enthuse, Lin did so, and April looked gratified.

' It is rather stunning, isn't it? Of course, I suppose you realize I turned the whole house over to a firm of interior decorators two weeks after Godfrey brought me here?' She laughed. ' I think the final bill staggered even Godfrey, but I must say he paid up like a lamb. And of course he had to admit the result was well worth it.'

' Y-yes,' Lin said slowly. The firm that April had employed had certainly done their work well, ignoring the second-rate and the mediocre and laying their hands with sure and certain instinct upon only the best. But there was still something wrong. She did not know what it was, it defied analysis. Unless . . . unless it was the very perfection that was out of place. Buonaventura was surely nothing if not a family home: it seemed to cry out for children and scattered toys and scuffed furniture and worn carpets. Did houses have souls? She smiled wryly to herself. Of course they didn't. But if they did a firm of interior decorators would probably be the last to find out.

April was flicking desultorily through the pages of a glossy magazine. Lin tried half-heartedly to make conversation by relating news of mutual friends, but though April showed a faint flicker of interest when she heard about Ann's engagement it was obvious that most of the time she was not really listening. Lin, herself very tired and badly worried to boot—if only she *knew* whether that wretched bag was safe! —could not help but feel thankful when at last her hostess, yawning unashamedly, proposed an early night.

Her first evening in Tobago had turned out rather differently from what she had expected, she reflected ruefully as she climbed the wide polished stairs to her bedroom. Her brow puckered in the anxious frown that Ann would have instantly recognized. The situation here was far worse than she'd imagined. April was obviously bored and disgruntled—almost dangerously so—and somehow Lin did not believe that it was merely Godfrey's absence and Ruel's provocative behaviour which were the root cause of the trouble. There was something else badly wrong, but what it was she could not at the moment decide. Well, if she really had lost her bag she'd have plenty of opportunity to find out, for she certainly wouldn't be able to return to England until she'd somehow managed to earn the money for her fare!

After undressing she put out the light and drew the curtains. Opening the big windows wide, she stood for a long time looking towards the distant mountains, rising in moonlit splendour against a luminous sky. The evening breeze, warm upon her cheeks, wafted heady perfumes to her from the fragrant frangipani flowers and the other exotic blooms which grew in such luxurious profusion in the garden below. It was very quiet, except for the friendly click of the cicadas. How *could* April be anything but happy, living on this wonderful island? she marvelled, and sighed. Why was it that contentment and her cousin were such strangers to each other? She had said it herself—she was never satisfied. She was always craving something new, something different. And marriage had not changed her.

With another sigh Lin turned away from the window and got into bed. She switched on her small bedside lamp and picking up a book started to read. Tired though she was, she knew that she would have difficulty in getting to sleep. April was quite right, worrying *was* futile—but it was easier to give advice than to take it! Thoughts of the missing handbag would, she knew only too well, haunt her throughout the night.

She had not been reading for more than a few minutes when a faint clatter upon her still open window—she had not bothered to draw the curtains again—made her start up, her eyes widening. It sounded exactly as though someone had picked up a handful of loose gravel and thrown it at the glass.

Swiftly she got out of bed and wrapping a soft rose pink kimono around her she stepped out of the window on to the balcony. Almost immediately a startled exclamation rose to her lips. Standing just below her, his tall figure etched dark and satyr-like against the moonlit background, was Ruel Saxon! Instinctively she pulled the kimono tighter round her slender figure and shrank back. Then common sense reasserted itself.

'What do you want?' she asked in a furious whisper.

He must have seen her shrinking movement, for when he answered her there was undisguised mockery in his voice. 'Don't worry, my intentions are strictly honourable! You must forgive the some- what dramatic approach! The house is locked up and I didn't want to disturb Aunt Lou. I saw your light, so I knew you weren't asleep.'

'But what do you want?' Lin asked the question with even more indignation than before. Suppose the servants weren't asleep and she was caught in this ridiculous situation?

'To return your bag. I thought you might like to know it was safe,' Ruel said simply, and held up the brown leather bag for her to see.

Lin caught her breath, relief and incredulity struggling for utterance at one and the same time. 'But . . . but how? Joseph searched your car thoroughly, at least he said he did,' she stammered.

'Hush! Keep your voice down! It wasn't in the car. You'd left it at the Half Moon Hotel,' Ruel said calmly. 'When Joseph told me that it was missing I guessed where it would be.'

54

Lin stared at him. ' You went to fetch it?' The frank disbelief in her voice caused a faint smile to touch his lips, but it had gone in a moment.

' I did. But pray do not feel obligated on that account! I had to go into Scarborough anyway. Catch!'

The handbag came spinning through the air and with a strangled gasp Lin caught it, more by good luck than by judgment. Ruel raised his hand in a casual salute and turning on his heel strode away into the shadows. Lin was left clutching her bag and struggling with feelings that were such a chaotic mixture of relief, gratitude, hostility, suspicion and surprise that she knew she could not even attempt to disentangle them.

CHAPTER IV

At least it was due to Ruel that she slept like the proverbial log. Lin was forced to acknowledge this when in the morning she woke to find the sunshine streaming through the still uncurtained windows, making patterns of gold on the wall beside her bed. All was quiet. Stretching out her hand for her wrist-watch, which lay on the little bedside table, she discovered that this was perhaps hardly surprising—it wasn't yet seven o'clock and April had never been an early riser.

She got out of bed and went straight to the window. The garden was as still and peaceful in the early morning sunshine as it had been in the moonlight of the previous night, and the only sign of life was a large tabby cat stretched out in the middle of the lawn. The sparkling, sweet-scented morning seemed to be beckoning her to come outside, but although she washed and dressed she resisted the temptation. Instead, she sat on the balcony, staring out into the garden with unseeing eyes and wondering once more about the problem of April . . . and the enigma that was her stepson. What had prompted Ruel to act as he had last night? He must have guessed how worried she would be about her missing handbag . . . and he had gone out of his way to put her mind at rest. She tugged at her hair with a puzzled frown. Why? Why had he bothered? It seemed completely out of character!

A sudden volley of barking and the sound of running feet jolted her rudely out of her reverie. She jumped up and looked over the balcony railing. The garden, formerly so empty and peaceful, suddenly seemed overpoweringly full of a small girl with long brown pigtails and a blue shirt and a large, shaggy dog of obscure pedigree. The cat had disappeared, but it was not difficult to guess at its whereabouts, for the dog was leaping futilely up and down at the foot of a small tree, hurling abuse into the branches.

' Oh, Argos, do be quiet! You'll wake everyone up!' The small girl's agonized protest made Lin's mind up for her. This must be Mandy, and now seemed an opportune moment to become acquainted. She was just debating whether she should call out when the child looked up and saw her. Lin saw her eyes widen and heard her horrified ' Oh *no*!' before she turned and fled precipitately across the lawn.

Argos, with one last frantic bark at his enemy, rushed helter-skelter after her.

'Now why did she do that?' Lin was half amused, half indignant. Was it possible that Mandy was as unsociable as her wretched brother? Well, there was only one way of finding out! Swiftly she tiptoed down the wide shallow staircase and made her way out into the garden through the big French doors in the dining room. As she had half expected, there was now no sign of either Mandy or the obstreperous Argos. For a moment she stood irresolute, then a flash of blue among the frangipani bushes at the bottom of the garden gave her the clue she needed. Evidently Mandy liked playing hide and seek! she thought with a grin. She sauntered casually up to the frangipani, then pounced.

'Got you!' she said, laughing and barring the way as Mandy made a futile attempt to dash past her. 'Down, Argos!' as the dog leapt up at her, barking loudly. 'Heavens, Mandy, does he think I'm that wretched cat?'

The child, who had been wriggling violently, darted her a quick look, then, surprisingly, stood still. Lin immediately released her, then stood back to look at her more closely. A weird kid, April had said—not a bit pretty. Well no, perhaps not, by April's standards. But the small pointed face was arrestingly alive: it held, Lin thought, far more than the promise of mere prettiness.

She said, 'You *are* Mandy, aren't you? Why did you run away? I was dying for someone to talk to!'

Mandy stared at her. 'You mean—we didn't wake you up?'

'Certainly not! I'd been awake for ages!'

Mandy heaved a sigh of relief. 'Then April won't be wild with poor Argos! She doesn't like him, you see: she says he's too noisy.' As if afraid that Lin might agree she added defensively, 'It's only that cat. It wouldn't be natural if he didn't want to chase it, would it?'

'Oh, very poor-spirited!' Lin assured her.

Mandy regarded her with great grey-green eyes which held an unmistakable gleam of approval. 'You're April's cousin, aren't you? She said you were coming. Why have you got up so early?'

'Because it's such a shame to waste a glorious morning lying in bed,' Lin told her, smiling.

'That's just what I think,' Mandy agreed. 'But April doesn't think so. She doesn't get up till ever so late. Do—do you think *she* heard Argos?'

'Most unlikely,' Lin said, thinking rather wryly of the many mornings she had almost had to shake her sleeping cousin into a state of awareness. Getting April up had always been a major task. She bent down and patted the dog's shaggy head. 'He's a nice old chap, isn't he? Is he your very own? What made you call him Argos?'

'Because of Ulysses' dog. You know—he died of joy when Ulysses came home from Troy,' Mandy explained.

'I didn't know, I'm afraid. Who told you about Ulysses?' Lin asked, amused.

'Ruel, of course. My brother. He gave me Argos for my last birthday.' Mandy paused, then delved into the pocket of her well-worn jeans. 'Are you hungry? I grabbed a couple of bananas when

I came out. Would you like one?'

It was definitely an overture of friendship. Lin realized with relief that she had been sized up and not found wanting. She accepted one of the bananas gratefully and she and Mandy sat side by side on a fallen log, munching in companionable silence.

Mandy finished her banana first. 'What are you going to do today? Do you like swimming?'

'I love it,' Lin said warmly, and Mandy's face lit up. 'So do I! Are you awfully good?'

'I wasn't too bad once. I'm horribly out of practice now,' Lin said ruefully.

'I swim like a fish.' It was said without a trace of conceit: she was merely stating a fact. 'Shall I show you my favourite beach after breakfast? It's rather a long way away, but it's worth the fag 'cos nobody else ever goes there. Oh!—but April will probably want you to do things with her, won't she?' and the small face shadowed.

'Perhaps April would like to come too,' Lin said quickly.

Mandy shook her head. 'She won't. She doesn't like the water. I 'spect she's afraid that awful stuff she puts on her eyes will all go funny.'

Lin decided it was time to change the subject. 'What shall we do with the banana skins?'

'Bury them.' Mandy began scraping a small hole in the ground with her short, square fingers, and Lin and Argos were helping her when a deep voice from behind them said, 'What *are* you doing? Looking for hidden treasure—or trying to dispose of the body?'

'Ruel!' Mandy's face was suddenly irradiated.

59

Looking at her, Lin wondered how on earth April could think she was plain. She flung herself into her brother's arms. ' You got up before me! Why didn't you wake me?'

' Because you went to bed far too late last night. I thought you needed your beauty sleep,' Ruel told her. He swung her off her feet to plant a kiss on the small freckled nose and Lin saw with a shock of almost incredulous surprise that the grey eyes were no longer hard and unfriendly.

Mandy suddenly remembered her manners. ' Have you met April's cousin? I don't know her name, but she's nice.'

' Yes, we've met,' Ruel said coolly. ' Good morning, Miss Grierson. You're abroad early.'

' Miss Grierson? Is that what you're called? What's your Christian name?' Mandy demanded.

' You can call me Lin.' She looked at Ruel, and found that the smile had already left his eyes. Was it only Mandy who had the power to turn him into a human being? She said, stammeringly, ' I—I didn't have a chance last night to thank you for——'

' Don't bother,' Ruel interrupted her with a brusqueness that verged on rudeness. ' Just be more careful of your property in future. You might not be so lucky next time you leave things lying around.'

' Oh!' Lin gasped, then stiffened. The old resentment of his dictatorial attitude rose swift and hot within her. She was darned if she'd feel grateful to this arrogant creature! Probably he'd only returned her bag in order to put her at a disadvantage!

Mandy had been looking from one to the other, a slightly puzzled expression creeping into her big eyes. She said, a little too loudly, ' She likes swimming, Ruel. She's not a bit like April, is she? I *do* think that's lucky!'

There was no mistaking her meaning, and Lin flushed scarlet. ' Mandy!' she exclaimed in distress.

' Mandy believes in saying what she thinks,' Ruel drawled. He paused, then added lightly, ' I wonder if she's right? You certainly don't *look* like April, but appearances can be deceptive.'

Lin's eyes were sparkling with anger. ' That's true. You *look* like a gentleman.'

To her surprise he gave a grim chuckle. ' Well, you've certainly got more brains than April! She wouldn't have thought of that one in a million years!'

Before Lin could answer he had turned to Mandy. ' Don't you think it's time for breakfast, honeychile?' The endearment, Lin noticed, seemed to come easily to his lips.

At once Mandy was all eagerness. ' Can I help you cook it?' She hesitated, then looked at Lin. ' You come and have breakfast with us too, Lin!'

' I must get back to the house. April will be wondering where I've got to,' Lin said, rather curtly.

' Oh no, she won't! April doesn't have breakfast till much later, in bed on a tray. *Do* come in, Lin! Ruel cooks super pancakes!' Mandy urged hospitably.

Lin saw with almost malicious pleasure that Ruel looked slightly put out. ' You can make the coffee this morning. What about making a start?' he suggested, and with a shriek of joy Mandy darted off, followed, inevitably, by Argos.

Ruel looked at Lin. 'Forgive me if I don't second Mandy's invitation. You appear to have made a conquest, but I'm sure my lovely stepmother would never forgive me if I attempted to monopolize her guest,' he said gently.

The colour surged into Lin's face. 'Do you think it's fair to keep on sniping at April? Especially in front of Mandy! It would be far wiser if you encouraged her to get on better with her stepmother!' she said hotly.

'Unfortunately April herself makes that course very difficult.' Ruel's face was once again bleak and granite hard. Lin, suppressing an indignant exclamation, swung on her heel to leave him, but to her surprise he caught hold of her arm, detaining her.

'Lin!' He used her Christian name for the first time and his voice sounded suddenly different. It was not until later—much later—that she realized the peremptory note had been missing. 'I don't know how much influence you've got with April, but if you've got any at all I advise you to persuade her to see a lot less of Luis Cortes than she has been doing!'

Lin caught her breath. 'Just on your say-so? I'm sorry, Ruel! I'm not in the habit of allowing myself to be blinded by other people's personal prejudices!'

'Prejudices?' Ruel stared at her, then gave a short laugh. 'My objections to Luis Cortes are based on far more than prejudice, I can assure you of that!'

Lin said coldly, 'Do you really think that April's friendships are any of *your* business?'

'In this instance—yes!' Ruel snapped. 'Oh, I know all about birds of a feather, but——'

He got no further. Lin said furiously, 'Do you always have to be so damned officious? You should be a policeman, not a painter!'

She heard Ruel suck in his breath and he took a step forward. 'Officious? Why, you little . . .'

'Massah Ruel!' That was Joseph's voice, and Lin, who had been conscious of a sudden thrill of very real apprehension, turned tail and fled back to the house. Just what that expression on Ruel's hard brown face had portented she did not know, but she had an uneasy feeling that he could be a dangerous adversary!

Despite the banana Mandy had given her she was very hungry, and did full justice to the excellent breakfast she found waiting for her. Afterwards she wrote a short letter to Ann who would, she knew, be anxious to hear from her and then she went in search of Aunt Lou to ask about postal arrangements. She found her in the big sunny kitchen, preparing a breakfast tray for April.

'I'll take it up. Yes, please, I'd like to!' as Aunt Lou, fat, kind and cheerful, demurred. 'I haven't seen my cousin this morning yet.' She cast an experienced eye over the contents of the tray. Fruit juice—dry toast—black coffee. No wonder April kept her sylph-like figure!

'Will you take the mail too, Missy?' Aunt Lou handed her two lettters and as Lin took them she couldn't help noticing that one of them bore a New York postmark. Almost certainly it was from Godfrey . . . perhaps it was to say when he was coming home. Surely that wretched lawsuit couldn't drag on much longer? When he returned presumably there'd be no need for Ruel to stay at Buonaventura any longer . . . he could return to the solitary life he seemed to prefer. It would certainly be good riddance . . . except that Mandy would obviously miss him badly. She frowned to herself. It was such a pity that there was so little love lost between April and her little stepdaughter. She'd like to believe that Mandy had merely taken her cue from Ruel, but honesty compelled her to admit that April had probably done nothing to win Mandy's affection. She'd made it abundantly clear that she didn't want to be bothered with a child. And she'd got Mandy all wrong . . . self-sufficient she might be, in many ways, but she was also full of warmth and affection. Unlike Ruel!

April's bedroom, with its silk-covered walls, pure white carpet and glittering array of silver and crystal on the dressing table, was rather like something out of the Arabian Nights, Lin thought as she knocked and entered. April herself was still asleep, but struggled up at the sound of Lin's voice, looking ethereal and fragile and far lovelier than anyone had the right to look immediately after waking up.

' What's the time? How long have you been up?' she asked drowsily.

' Ages!' Lin told her. ' I was out in the garden long before breakfast.' She hesitated, then added casually, ' I met Mandy.'

' Oh? What did you think of her?' April's voice betrayed a complete lack of interest.

' Rather a pet.'

'No accounting for tastes,' April said, yawning. She began sipping her fruit juice. 'Had she got that frightful hound with her?'

'Argos? She had. But why is he frightful? I thought he was rather a pet, too,' Lin said, laughing.

April frowned. 'My dear, it's a ghastly animal! The spaniels are bad enough, heaven knows, but Argos . . . ! I try to discourage her from bringing him into the house, great clumsy animal, but of course she doesn't take any notice of what *I* say!' She caught sight of the letters Lin was still holding in her hand and there was a sudden note of eagerness in her voice as she asked 'Are those for me?'

'Yes.' Lin handed her the letters, but rather to her surprise April ignored the one with the U.S. postmark. Instead she ripped open the second one, which was addressed in a bold, flowing hand, with what seemed to be almost feverish haste. Lin, turning away to draw the curtains and to pick up the clothes that lay scattered on the floor—April hadn't learnt to be any tidier, she thought wryly—realized when she went back to her cousin's side that whoever the letter was from it was evidently more than welcome. Her cheeks were slightly flushed and a tiny smile was playing around her lovely, provocative mouth.

She felt Lin's gaze on her, and hurriedly stuffed the letter back into its envelope. She said lightly, 'It's from Luis. Just to say he's sorry about last night.' Before Lin could comment she had picked up the second letter.

'I suppose this is from Godfrey.' She tore it

open, this time in a far more leisurely fashion. She scanned the two closely-written pages in silence, then flung them down almost pettishly. ' Heavens, I can't wade through all that tarradiddle now! The main thing is that he hopes to be home in time for my birthday. That's next week as ever was.' She gave a hard, brittle laugh. ' I'd better make the most of what remains of my freedom, hadn't I?'

Lin bit her lip. April didn't mean it, of course, but . . . Desperately she tried to stifle the uneasy suspicion that had grown in her mind as she watched April read Luis' letter.

April saw her troubled expression and laughed again. ' Lin, you goose! Don't you know yet when I'm joking?' She jumped out of bed and stretched her brown arms above her head.

' Light me a cigarette, will you, Lin? They're on my dressing table.'

Lin looked at her. April had once smoked only occasionally, now she was virtually a chain smoker.

' You smoke far too much, April,' she protested, and immediately annoyance quivered across her cousin's lovely face. ' Don't preach, coz!' she said shortly. ' I get enough of that from Godfrey—not to mention that precious stepson of his!'

She disappeared into the bathroom. ' I suppose you want to go and see about your handbag before we do anything else?' she called out.

Lin hesitated. Somehow she felt oddly reluctant to tell April about her midnight encounter with Ruel Saxon, but obviously she had to know that the handbag had been recovered.

' No need. I've got it back.' She tried hard

66

to sound casual, but knew that she did not quite succeed.

There was a moment's silence, then April emerged, a fluffy white towel wrapped round her slender figure, her eyes wide with astonishment.

'You've got it back?'

'Yes.' Reluctantly Lin explained, and realized at once, with a sinking heart, that April was far from pleased.

'Ruel playing knight errant?' She gave a nasty laugh. 'Well, don't let it impress you too much.'

'I won't.' Lin spoke with such fervour that April's face cleared.

'Well, perhaps it's a good thing you've got it back, because I didn't really want to go into Scarborough this morning, anyway. Some friends of Godfrey's have invited us to lunch and I suppose we may as well play bridge this afternoon. Cocktails tonight, with some people Luis introduced me to. I don't know them well, but anyone Luis knows is bound to be fun.'

Lin said nothing. The programme didn't really appeal: she would have infinitely preferred to go swimming or explore the island, but there was nothing much she could do about it. She and April had always had widely divergent tastes and interests.

She discovered, during the next few days, that since April's marriage the gulf had grown even wider, and her disquietude increased. She couldn't help feeling that if April really was as bored and lonely as she had made out it was partly her own fault, for none of the natural attractions of the island seemed to appeal to her in the slightest. She didn't like swimming, sailing or snorkeling: she was indifferent to the wonderful scenery and bird life: she was even reluctant to sunbathe for fear of spoiling her flawless magnolia complexion. Peace and solitude bored her to smithereens, and the only times she seemed really happy were when she was spending money. She made frequent shopping expeditions and her extravagance almost shocked Lin, who had been accustomed from childhood to 'making do', though she consoled herself with the reflection that at least April could afford her profligacy!

There were other disturbing factors. April had always been capricious, but now her moods alternated between wild gaiety and almost sullen silences, for which Lin was at a loss to account. Luis was still away: of Ruel they saw nothing. His bungalow might have been one hundred miles away instead of only one hundred yards. Lin wondered a little ruefully whether he was taking very good care to avoid the adult inhabitants of Buonaventura; if so, she should be profoundly thankful, for she had soon realized that even the mere mention of Ruel's name acted as an irritant to April.

They saw very little, too, of Mandy. Lin regretted this, though it was obvious that April's feelings on the matter were quite different. It was not, Lin thought, that April meant to be unkind: she merely made it embarrassingly clear that she considered her ready-made family something of a nuisance. Luckily for Mandy everyone else seemed to adore her. Perhaps that was half the trouble, Lin thought wryly. April did not enjoy playing second fiddle, even to a young child.

Mandy so patently avoided her stepmother whenever she could that Lin was startled, on returning one evening from another of April's interminable shopping expeditions, to find the child waiting for them with every sign of burning impatience. Directly she caught sight of the car she hurled herself down the steps, and as April got out she clutched hold of her arm with agonized fingers.

'April! Oh, April! Argos is sick! Please will you come and have a look at him? Aunt Lou and Joseph don't know what's wrong with him and—and I'm frightened.'

It was obvious that in her overwhelming anxiety she had forgotten all about the antagonism she usually felt towards her stepmother. Now, Lin thought, was April's chance—and she held her breath.

April's brows drew together in a frown as she disengaged herself from Mandy's clutching fingers. 'Sick? Since when?'

'This afternoon.' Mandy choked back a sob. 'We went out for a walk and he seemed all right until just before we got back. Then he was all flopped out and—and panting. He had lots to drink and then—and then he crawled into a corner and went to sleep. But it isn't a proper sleep—I just know there's something awfully queer about him.'

April was still frowning. 'Doesn't Ruel know what's wrong with him?'

'He isn't here. He's gone to Trinidad, he won't be back until tomorrow.' Mandy looked up at her with big imploring eyes. 'Oh, please come quickly, April!'

'Oh, really, Mandy! I know nothing at all about sick animals!' April's voice was sharpened by impatience. She had had a frustrating afternoon, looking in vain for gloves and handbag to match a suit she had fallen in love with, and she was hot and tired. Lin saw the piteous expression on the child's face and stepped forward quickly.

'Shall I come, Mandy? I don't know a lot, I'm afraid, but I can probably tell you whether he's just a little bit sick or—or whether it's rather more serious.'

Mandy wasted no more time on her stepmother. Leaving April staring after them, she caught hold of Lin's hand and almost dragged her to a small morning-room, where Argos lay limply in a corner. Lin, falling on to her knees beside his basket, realized at once that the dog, who lay with glazed eyes and panting breath, was unconscious.

She looked up into Mandy's frightened face. 'He needs help, Mandy—at once. I—I think he's probably been poisoned. Is there a vet anywhere near here?' What a hopeless question, she thought despairingly. Buonaventura was situated in the wildest part of the island.

Mandy's eyes were enormous in her pale face. 'I think there's someone in Louisville. It—it's a little village about ten miles from here.' She stopped, frantically searching her memory for information which might spell life for Argos. 'I believe he's called Bob. He—he isn't a vet, but he knows an awful lot about animals. Daddy had him for one of the dogs once and—and he got better.'

'Then I'm going to fetch him.' Lin rose to her

70

feet with decision. 'I'll borrow April's car, she won't mind. No, you'd better stay with Argos, Mandy.'

'You'll be quicker if you have someone with you who knows the way.' The despair in Mandy's eyes was giving way to a dawning hope. Something about Lin's purposeful manner inspired her with confidence.

'Very true! I'll take Joseph.'

A few minutes later Mandy heard the car start and knew that Lin had started on her desperate errand.

'Oh, please let her find Bob! Please let them be in time!' she thought, casting a terror-stricken look at the suffering dog, who even to her eyes seemed to be growing weaker every minute. 'Oh, if only Ruel was here!'

Luck was with Lin. With Joseph at her side she had no difficulty in finding the right village, though because she was unfamiliar with the tortuous winding roads she dared not drive as fast as she would have liked. She had feared that they would have some difficulty in locating Bob, but she needn't have worried, for the first person she asked directed them to a tumbledown shack at the far end of the village. Bob turned out to be a big burly Tobagan with a broad, impassive face and the whitest teeth Lin had ever seen. He listened in silence to her breathless explanation, then without a word reached for his hat. It was a bowler, and perched incongruously on top of his curly head, but it was, as Lin later learnt, a prestige symbol, like his big horn-rimmed spectacles.

Half an hour later they were back at Buonaventura, and Bob was bending over the sick animal, handling his poor limp body with a deft gentleness which impressed Lin as she watched, fetching and carrying under his softly-spoken directions. Argos seemed to respond almost at once to his treatment, though it seemed like hours before Bob rose to his feet with what sounded like a sigh of satisfaction.

' It's been touch and go, but with a bit of luck he'll pull through now. He'll need careful watching for a time, though,' and he gave one or two directions to Lin.

When he had gone Mandy burst into tears for the first time.

' Mandy, dear!' Lin held her closely. ' Don't cry! Didn't you hear what Bob said? He's going to be all right now!'

' Y-yes, I know, but . . .' Mandy dashed the tears from her eyes with the back of her hand and contrived to give Lin a watery smile. ' It's just that I'm so *glad*! I—I couldn't have borne it if Argos had died, Lin!'

' Well, there's no fear of that now,' Lin said reassuringly. She glanced at her watch. ' Heavens, is that really the time? Bed for you, my child! There's nothing else you can do for Argos, and you look as though you could do with a good night's sleep,' for Mandy's pale little face showed signs of the strain she had undergone during the last few hours.

Mandy looked at her reproachfully. ' You don't think I'm going to leave him, do you? I'm going to stay up with him all night! You heard what Bob said—he needs careful watching.'

' But I'm going to stay up with him,' Lin told her

quietly. 'There's no need for the two of us.'

Mandy stared at her incredulously. 'You really mean that? You'd really do that for Argos?'

'For Argos—and for you,' Lin told her.

Mandy caught her breath and her eyes were suspiciously bright. 'Oh, Lin, you *are* nice!' she said naively. 'But—but Argos is my dog! I ought to stay up with him, not you. Please let me!'

'I really think it would be better if you went to bed. Argos may need you tomorrow, and what will happen if you're so tired that you can't look after him properly?'

The logic of this argument won the day. For a moment Lin thought that Mandy was going to rebel, then she suddenly capitulated.

'All right, I'll go to bed if you really want me to. But you do promise you won't leave him?' she asked anxiously.

'Promise!' Lin assured her, and Mandy heaved a sigh of relief. Before she went she suddenly flung her arms round Lin's neck. '*Thank* you!' she whispered, and Lin, returning her hug, knew that she had won a friend for life. But oh, if only it had been April who had come to the rescue! Even though she didn't like Argos it had still been the best chance she was ever likely to have of gaining Mandy's confidence and affection—and she had thrown it away. Mandy would always remember, now, that when she had asked April for help it had been refused.

She sighed. April had given grudging permission for her car to be used for the journey to Louisville, but she hadn't bothered to come and enquire how Argos was. •

'Lin!' Just at that moment the door burst open and April stormed in. 'What *are* you still doing? I've been waiting and waiting for you to come and alter that blue dress of mine! You promised you'd do it tonight!'

'Oh, April, I'm sorry!' Lin looked up in dismay. 'I'd forgotten all about it. But you don't want to wear it tomorrow, do you?'

'I might.' April's voice was querulous. 'Anyway that's not the point. I invited you out here to be company for me, not to look after sick mongrels!' For the first time she glanced at Argos. 'Can't you leave that wretched dog alone now? Is he any better?'

'Oh, much!' Lin, inwardly dismayed by April's attitude, spoke cheerfully. 'But—I hope you don't mind, April—I'm going to sleep down here tonight, in that armchair, so as to be at hand if I'm wanted. I don't think there's any danger now, but just in case——'

April stared at her. 'Are you crazy? Losing a good night's sleep over that wretched animal? I've never heard of anything so silly! I'm—I'm *sorry* he's better! He'd have been no loss to anyone if he'd died!'

Lin would have said that she knew April too well to be surprised by anything she did or said, but for a moment she could not believe the evidence of her own ears. She dared not trust herself to speak, but the look she gave April pulled that damsel up in her tracks. During the years they had lived together Lin, out of consideration for her aunt, had only rarely lost her temper with her cousin, but April had

74

reason to remember those few occasions still.

She gave an uneasy laugh and there was a more conciliatory note in her voice as she said, ' Oh, all right, I didn't mean it! Stay up with the dog if you want to. I suppose you've got no objections if *I* go to bed?' Without waiting for an answer she flounced off, leaving Lin staring after her, her lips rather firmly compressed. She was angrier with April than she had ever been before. She had once passionately refuted Ann's claim that April had no heart—yet how *could* her cousin, knowing what Argos meant to Mandy, have possibly said that she was sorry he was better?

She bowed her head on to her hands. April must have changed even more than she had thought.

CHAPTER V

Argos seemed to recover with amazing rapidity. After a day or two he was so much his old self again that when one morning April suddenly proposed that Lin and Mandy should take a picnic lunch and spend the day together on the beach there was never any question of his being left behind.

Both Lin and Mandy were delighted by April's unexpected proposal: Mandy because she was longing to show Lin her favourite haunt—a beautiful secluded bay—and Lin because it would be her first real taste of freedom. April made it clear that she did not intend to join the party: she had, she said, an appointment in Scarborough with her hairdresser and she didn't know how long she'd be.

' I don't suppose you want to hang about waiting for me. It will be much nicer for you to go swimming with Mandy, won't it?' she said pleasantly. ' I'll drop you at the bay on my way into Scarborough and pick you up later this afternoon, about four.'

Lin, rather startled by April's sudden amiability, agreed. Perhaps, she thought, April was trying to make amends for her ill-judged outburst the night that Argos had been so ill. She had certainly been rather subdued ever since—well, until this morning, at any rate. At the moment she seemed to be in extraordinarily good spirits: in fact, there was almost a glow of excitement about her. Lin was rather puzzled as to the cause, but couldn't help hoping that the mood would last. April could be so charming when she wanted to be and even Mandy, usually tongue-tied in her stepmother's company, seemed to find her gaiety infectious.

The road to the bay wound its way through wild scenery and was rough, stony and, towards the end, almost precipitous. It was a somewhat spectacular ride. April, cheerfully disregarding the possibility of a broken axle, took them most of the way, but since the only road leading down to the beach was a narrow stone trail almost overgrown by cactus and thornbush she was forced to drop them at the top and let them make their own way from there. It was, Lin thought ruefully, nothing if not a hazardous descent—no wonder Mandy had said the bay was usually deserted!—but scratched and breathless though she was at the end of the trail, she had to admit that the effort was well worthwhile.

The beach was a deserted wide sweep of snowy-white sand, lined all the way with palm trees. The sea itself looked incredibly clear and inviting. There were no waves to speak of and though in the shallows the water was green, further out the bay was a glorious blue. It was the loveliest, most peaceful place Lin thought she'd ever seen.

'It's heaven!' she said rapturously.

It was almost that. She and Mandy swam in the warm translucent water and romped with Argos on the silver sand. They ate their picnic lunch under the shade of a palm tree while Argos gambolled and frisked around them, and then they lazed in the sunshine before they swam again. As Mandy had said, she was an excellent swimmer and seemed to be as much at home in the water as she was on dry land.

'You're a mermaid—or a water-baby!' Lin told her after a race in which Mandy had beaten her with disconcerting ease.

'But you're very good,' Mandy said generously. 'Much better than I thought you'd be. You only need a bit of practice, then I'd probably have a job to beat you.' She stopped, eyeing her anxiously. 'Are you sure you're all right, Lin? You've gone awfully pale.'

'Of course.' Lin forced a reassuring smile. In actual fact she had agreed to the race rather against her better judgment and the effort had left her feeling completely exhausted. Rest and sunshine had done wonders for her since she had come to Tobago—she was hardly coughing at all now—but she was still not as fit as she might be.

Mandy was lying on her tummy, propped up by her elbows. She said, ' It was Ruel who taught me how to swim. Sometimes when he's not too busy he takes me snorkeling. I love that.' She turned her head and glanced at Lin. ' Have you ever been underwater ? It's super.'

Lin shook her head regretfully and Mandy added, ' I'll ask Ruel to take us both.'

Lin felt herself flushing. Evidently Mandy didn't realize that Ruel's hostility towards April embraced her cousin also! She said quickly, ' I shouldn't do that. Ruel won't want to be bothered with me.'

' Yes, he will.' Mandy spoke with absolute confidence. Then she hesitated. ' He—he's awfully kind, you know, Lin.'

' Is he?' Lin spoke with a bitterness which she had not meant to display, especially to Mandy.

Mandy shot her a quick look. ' Has April been saying things to you? She doesn't like him, but I guess that's only because he can see right through her.'

' Mandy!' Lin sat up and spoke firmly. ' I'm sorry, I can't allow you to speak about April in that way.'

Mandy's face wore a closed obstinate look, but she did not argue the point. Instead she jumped up. ' I'm going in again. Coming?'

' Too lazy. Besides, I'm going to get dressed in a minute. April will be here pretty soon.'

She closed her eyes. The sand was soft and warm and the sun was caressing her back. It would be hard not to fall asleep.

An excited bark from Argos roused her and she

sat up quickly. The dog was racing madly across the sand towards a tall, oddly familiar figure. Her heart gave a queer inexplicable lurch. Blinking her eyes against the glare of the sun and almost holding her breath, she waited for the man to come closer so that she could distinguish his features more clearly. It wasn't—it couldn't be—yes, it *was*! Ruel!

Her cheeks scarlet, Lin clutched for a towel. What on earth was Ruel doing here? she thought confusedly, furious with herself for feeling so absurdly self-conscious. Heavens, here in Tobago a swimming suit was practically the national costume!

As he came up to her, Argos still barking excitedly at his heels, she suddenly thought that he looked tired. She knew that the management of Godfrey's enormous plantations was no sinecure and that usually he worked long hours—which made his presence here on the beach, at four o'clock in the afternoon, even more puzzling.

Ruel answered her unspoken question immediately. 'I had a telephone call from April.' His voice was quiet and expressionless. 'She's been unavoidably delayed in town and won't be home until late.'

'So she asked you to collect us?' April seemed to make a habit of shifting her responsibilities off on to other people's shoulders, Lin thought grimly. First Luis, and now Ruel!

'Well, it's rather a long way to walk back to Buonaventura,' Ruel pointed out, and unbelievably he was smiling.

With fingers that trembled a little Lin began to slip her cotton frock over her bathing suit, which had dried out in the sun. To her annoyed embarrassment a button became entangled in her long hair and despite her desperate tugs she could not free herself.

'Allow me.' She felt Ruel's strong, warm hands on her shoulders and stood rigid while he disentangled her. When at last, breathless and somewhat dishevelled, she turned to thank him she found him looking at her with an odd expression in his grey eyes.

Without preamble he said quietly, 'It is I who should thank you, Lin. Mandy has told me what you did for her and Argos the other night. I'd like you to know that I'm very grateful to you. It would have broken Mandy's heart if anything had happened to Argos.'

Lin was scarlet. 'I was glad to be of help.' The warmth in Ruel's eyes and voice had knocked her completely off balance. So nonplussed was she by his unexpected amiability that she could only stand there, dumbly staring.

Just at that moment Mandy came rushing up to them. 'Have you come instead of April to collect us, Ruel? How super!' She flung herself on her brother, words tumbling out of her mouth in her anxiety to tell him everything at once. 'We've had a simply marvellous time! Lin can swim awfully well, we had a race and she nearly beat me. She wants to skin-dive: will you take us, please?'

'Mandy!' Lin exclaimed, but Ruel only laughed. 'I don't see why not.' He looked at Lin. 'I'll take you to Arnos Vale if you like. It has to be seen to be believed.'

Lin met his gaze squarely. 'You don't owe me

anything, Ruel. What I did was for Mandy, not for you.'

It was a moment before he answered, and when he did so he seemed to be weighing his words. 'I don't doubt that. But you're wrong about one thing, Lin. I do owe you something—an apology.' He hesitated, then said ruefully, 'I guess I just wouldn't let myself believe that anyone belonging to—that you were so nice.'

He'd been going to say that he wouldn't let himself believe that anyone belonging to April could be so nice, Lin thought, and tried to whip up a feeling of resentment on April's behalf. But Ruel was speaking again, and the coaxing note in his voice was almost irresistible.

'I hope you'll let me make amends for my— ungentlemanly—conduct.'

Before Lin could answer Mandy, bored by a conversation she could not fully comprehend, had tugged impatiently at their hands.

'Come on! Let's go home! Have you packed everything in the picnic basket, Lin?'

Lin assented, glad to turn her mind to everyday practicalities. Ruel, having made his apology, seemed content to leave things as they were and it was in complete silence that they began the steep climb up to the road. Mandy, with Argos, led the way, as sure-footed as a mountain goat, and Lin and Ruel followed. To her chagrin Lin found herself short of breath long before they reached the top and once or twice she missed her footing. The second time she slithered backwards amidst a shower of falling stones and the next moment she felt Ruel take her hand.

'I'll help you up.'

'No, please . . . I can manage.' She tried to disengage her fingers, but Ruel was clasping them too tightly. Her breathlessness now was not entirely due to the steepness of the climb and she was immeasurably relieved when they reached the top.

'Thank you,' she said stiffly.

Was there a fugitive glint of amusement in the grey eyes? She could not be sure, for already he was walking towards his white Chevrolet, which was parked on the side of the road. Mandy, appropriating the off front seat after Lin had hastily assured her that she preferred to sit in the back, chatted gaily all the way back to Buonaventura, leaving Lin to her chaotic thoughts. What was the reason for the extraordinary change in Ruel's attitude? Merely that he was grateful for the help she had given Mandy? Or had he meant what he said on the beach? She did not know, but one thing was indisputable. Ruel knew only too well how to disarm . . . in fact, when that warm, delightful smile lit up his dark face he was almost dangerously attractive. She bit her lip. She mustn't allow herself to find him attractive. Apart from any other consideration, it wouldn't be fair to April.

When they reached Buonaventura Ruel stopped the car short of the house. Then he turned in his seat to look at Lin with lifted brows.

'April said she wouldn't be back until late. Do you really want to have tea in solitary splendour or will you come and take pot luck with Mandy and me?'

Of course she must refuse. Lin opened her mouth to do so and then saw the eager sparkle in Mandy's eyes.

' *Please*, Lin,' she coaxed.

It would have taken a much harder heart than Lin's to have withstood such an appeal. Almost to her horror she found herself accepting the invitation. ' What *will* April say?' she thought, then reflected that after all it was April herself who had set the present chain of events in motion!

As Ruel stood aside to let her and Mandy precede him into his bungalow she realized, somewhat shame-facedly, that she had been curious to know what it was like. It was small, comprising a bedroom, a large sitting room which seemed to be split into a working studio side and a living side, a bathroom and a tiny kitchen. After the luxury of Buon-aventura the whole seemed painfully bare and austere, but obviously that was the way Ruel liked it. Soft living and Ruel were somehow antithetical.

In the sitting room a few canvases were propped up against the wall. Lin looked at them and then, a little shyly, at Ruel.

' Yours?' She hesitated, even now half fearing a rebuff. ' May—may I see them?'

' Politeness or inclination?' Amazingly, the grey eyes were laughing at her again.

' Inclination.'

' Then you may look at them while Mandy and I get the tea,' Ruel told her, then, as she protested, ' Don't you trust a mere male to produce something edible?'

Lin found herself laughing back. ' You forget

that Mandy has already given you a glowing recommendation! It's just that I feel I ought to help.'

'Well, if you're very good we'll let you wash up,' Ruel said with a grin, and disappeared into the kitchen.

Left to herself, Lin looked carefully at the canvases. She did not know a great deal about art, but enough to know that Ruel's work was outstanding. All but one of the canvases were landscapes: the exception was a portrait of Mandy. It was not yet finished, but even so it completely captured the child's personality. This, surely, was Ruel's métier! She said so, impulsively, when Ruel brought in a large tray loaded with ham, lobster, fresh pineapples, asparagus, tomatoes, cucumber and lettuce, but he shook his head.

'I prefer painting places to people. They're usually nicer.'

'Oh, but that's a terrible thing to say!' Lin cried indignantly. Then she flushed vividly, for there was a disturbing expression in Ruel's eyes.

'There are exceptions,' he said softly.

'He liked painting me.' Mandy came in with a pile of plates. 'But you wouldn't paint April when she asked you to, would you, Ruel? She was frightfully cross!'

There was a tiny silence as with the mention of April constraint crept into the atmosphere for the first time. Then as if he hadn't heard Ruel began to talk, impersonally, of other things.

The meal was delicious. Afterwards Lin washed up while Ruel wiped and Mandy put the things away in a tiny cupboard which was a model of apple-pie order. There was no doubt, Lin thought wryly, about Ruel's self-sufficiency.

The chores finished, she would have returned to Buonaventura, but Mandy begged so hard for her to stay and make a third in a game of Monopoly that she gave in. It was lovely to see Mandy looking so happy, she thought: her pale little face flushed with excitement as she triumphantly erected hotels in Park Lane and Mayfair and her big eyes sparkling as she demanded extortionate dues from Lin and Ruel. Poor kid, she missed out on a lot, what with a father who was usually too busy to play with her, a stepmother who didn't like her and a brother who seemed content to spend most of his life on what was practically a desert island! Lin, remembering what her own lot would have been if Aunt Bea hadn't taken her in and given her the same care and affection she gave to her own daughter, felt a sudden spurt of anger. Whose fault was it if Mandy was growing up as wild as an Arawak? Given the right training she'd be an absolute darling!

Rashly, she said as much to Ruel after Mandy, tired out though indignantly protesting that she was nothing of the sort, had gone to bed. For a moment Ruel looked at her, his face inscrutable. Then he said quietly, ' I know. I'd hoped so much that April——' then he broke off as if he'd thought better of what he was going to say.

Lin did not challenge him. The last few hours had been the happiest she had spent for a long time, though she did not seek to reason why. All she knew was that she didn't want them to be spoilt by another row over April—especially as she would be hard put

85

to it to defend April's attitude towards Mandy, anyway.

She would have said goodnight and retreated into the drawing room to await April's return (where *was* she? she wondered) but Ruel barred her way.

'Why not make a night of it, Lin? April won't be back yet, you know. Will you come out with me? Is there anywhere you'd specially like to go?'

Lin caught her breath, surprised and a little alarmed by the sudden wave of emotion which had swept over her. An evening alone with Ruel—oh no, she ought not! April would never forgive her! But Ruel was smiling at her, and she thought of the alternative, sitting alone and lonely waiting for April's return, and threw caution to the winds. In for a penny, in for a pound! And at least she'd have an evening to remember!

So she thought then, but afterwards she could never recall the evening in detail. She only knew that its enchantment would stay with her for the rest of her life. They drove along in a clear night with a ceiling of stars above them, and the air was sweet-scented with night blooming jasmine and the fireflies, tiny points of phosphorescent light, lit their way with fairy lanterns. By the time they reached Scarborough—a town of glittering lights whose reflections swayed and bobbed, jewel-bright, in the dark waters of the bay—Lin's spirits were rocketing sky-high, and she knew that Ruel's mood matched her own.

She wondered, with amazement, why she had ever thought he was cold . . . brusque . . . arrogant. They talked as if they had known each other all their lives. She found herself telling him all about the air crash that had orphaned her when she was only a little older than Mandy, about the wonderful kindness of Aunt Bea, about her life in London. Only April was never mentioned.

And in his turn Ruel talked of his early years at Buonaventura and then of the little island which he had made his own. A tiny jewel of an island, he told her, too remote to be touched by modernity: set in a sun-flecked sea and possessing a multitude of different views, all different and yet all conveying the same sharp stab of beauty . . .

The only thing he did not tell her was the reason he had left Tobago. And Lin did not ask, though already in her mind the suspicion was forming that the story of Ruel's lost love might not be exactly as April had told it.

In Scarborough they had dinner somewhere which wasn't in the least fashionable but where the food was marvellous, and they listened to a steel band and, later, they danced. Then, driving along quiet, starlit roads, Ruel showed her the sleeping island and Lin felt as though she were in a dream . . . a dream woven of moonbeams, frangipani, stars, palm trees and the sound of the sea.

But even a dream had to end some time. When at last they returned to Buonaventura they sat for a moment in silence, looking at the stars. They were more brilliant and more numerous than Lin had ever imagined, the different constellations being almost lost in the shimmering dust of the sky. ' Untroubled sentries of the shadowy night,' she quoted softly, then roused herself.

' Ruel, what's the time, please? I ought to get in

before April. I—I didn't leave a message and she might worry.'

'April? Worry about anyone but herself?' Ruel's voice was ironic. Then, almost savagely, he added, 'Lin, why do you try so hard to fool yourself?'

Lin dug her fingers into the palms of her hands. Back to square one, she thought miserably. She said 'Ruel, please!' Then, desperately, 'Why do you hate her so? She—she's spoilt and—and a bit selfish, but she isn't *bad* . . .'

He said smoothly, 'Did she tell you I hated her?'

'She said you were jealous of her.' The words were out before Lin could stop herself.

He gave her a look of what she could have sworn was genuine astonishment. 'Jealous? Of April? For God's sake, *why?*'

She did not answer and he repeated the question, his voice hard.

'She—she thinks she's cut you out,' Lin stammered miserably. 'You—you must have thought that one day Buonaventura would be yours and now——' She stopped, unable to go on.

'So April thinks I'm eating my heart out over my ruined prospects! That is very, very amusing!' Ruel gave a short laugh, then added bitterly, 'But how like dear April to imagine that everyone is as money-grabbing as she is herself!'

'Ruel! That isn't fair!' Lin's protest was instinctive.

He looked at her, and suddenly his eyes were as hard and cold as agates.

'Why are you so loyal to April, Lin? Is it

88

because you consider it politic?'

'Politic?' Lin stared at him.

'Well, she *has* married a reputedly rich man, hasn't she?' Ruel drawled. 'I suppose it's natural for the poor relations to gather round her table, waiting for whatever crumbs may fall.'

The dream had turned into a nightmare. For a moment Lin could hardly believe her ears. Then, 'How *dare* you!' she gasped. For a moment rage almost choked her, then she hurled words at him like brickbats.

'I've never taken a *penny* from April, nor will I ever do so! I wouldn't *dream* of accepting the crumbs from her table, as you so delightfully put it! I couldn't care less about her money!' She stopped, her eyes brilliant with unshed tears, then she said between her teeth, 'And in case you think otherwise, I paid my own fare out here, though I'll admit that my board and lodging is free! Perhaps you think I should ask April to present me with a bill? Is that the way guests at Buonaventura usually behave?'

She felt two steel-like hands grip her shoulders and shake her. Ruel's voice, suddenly different, said, 'Lin, be quiet . . . listen . . .'

'I won't be quiet!' Lin struggled violently for self-control. 'If you really want to know why I'm loyal to April, you might stop to remember what I owe to her mother! And now, if you'll excuse me, I'm going in!'

'Lin . . . Lin, I'm sorry! I didn't mean to hurt you!' Ruel was speaking in a breathless, goaded undertone, almost as though the words were being wrenched from him against his will. 'God knows why I lashed out at you like that—you of all people! I didn't mean what I said, I swear I didn't! It's just that April—but hell, I needn't take it out on you!'

There was no mistaking the bitterness in his voice, almost amounting to self-loathing, nor the softened expression that put to rout the satyr look.

What he had said was unforgivable, whether he'd meant it or not. Lin knew that perfectly well, yet she also knew with wild certainty that when he looked like that, spoke like that, she would forgive Ruel Saxon almost anything.

Her voice shaking, she said, ' It's all right. But—but please don't criticize April to me again, Ruel. I—I can't bear it.'

Even though there was plenty of cause for criticism, she thought unhappily as she went into the house. Where was April now? And where had she been all day? And what would she say when she learnt—for of course she would have to be told—that Lin had been fraternizing with the enemy? Inevitably that was how she would look upon it, Lin had no doubts on that score.

Only Ruel wasn't *her* enemy. Staring at her reflection in the mirror as she brushed her hair with quick, nervous strokes, Lin forced herself to acknowledge the truth. It was hopeless, it was stupid, but nonetheless it had happened, and there was nothing on earth she could do about it. She had fallen head over heels in love with Ruel Saxon.

CHAPTER VI

For all her romanticism Lin did not attempt to persuade herself that Ruel reciprocated her feelings.
He had certainly exerted himself to be charming last
night—at least until April's name had cropped up
—but she felt reasonably sure that she meant no
more to him than a nice girl who had been kind to
his small sister. He had wanted to make amends
for the somewhat cavalier way in which he had
treated her: well, he had done so. He had given
her a wonderful evening and that was that. Finish.
Her wisest course now was to stop acting like a
stupidly romantic schoolgirl and to put him out of
her mind. After reaching this conclusion she lay
thinking about him until at last she fell into a
troubled sleep.

When she awoke, however, her first thought was
not for Ruel but for April. It must have been after
midnight when she'd heard her come in, and though
she had half thought of getting up she had decided
against it. Somehow she was reluctant to face April
while she was still under the heady influence of
moonlight and roses: it would be better to wait until
morning, when willy-nilly she would have to shake
out the stars from her eyes.

In the morning she was still somewhat apprehen-
sive about meeting her cousin—' Thus conscience
doth make cowards of us all!' she thought grimly—
but soon found that April was in her sunniest mood.
She apologized, charmingly, for her change of plans,

brought about, she said, by a chance meeting with a friend who had just returned to Tobago from a three-month holiday in New York.

'She was holding a sort of impromptu party to celebrate her homecoming—you know, rounding up everybody by phone,' April explained. 'Naturally I was invited. I—I did think of you, Lin, but I didn't suppose that you'd really feel much like partying after a day on the beach.'

The excuse was so typically April that in spite of herself Lin's lips twitched.

'Was it a good party?'

'M-m-m-m. Not bad.' April ran her slender fingers through the candyfloss of her hair. Then she added, with careful nonchalance, 'By the way, guess who was there? Luis. He's just got back from Jamaica, with a brand-new yacht. He's invited us both aboard for lunch to-day. You'd like to see him again, wouldn't you, Lin?'

Luis. For one unguarded moment Lin's face showed her surprise—and her disquiet. She'd almost persuaded herself that there'd been absolutely no need for Ruel to give her any advice about her cousin's friendship with Luis—April hadn't mentioned him for days and the only letters that had come to the house had been from Godfrey. But now he was back. She bit her lip. After last night . . . *did* she in fact want to see Luis again? Whatever the rights and wrongs of that old affair, wasn't she now ranged on Ruel's side? Then she gave herself an impatient little shake. Luis had looked after her when she'd first arrived in Tobago . . . been kind and considerate. Common sense dictated that she should think of him as April's friend rather than as Ruel's enemy.

April's friend. Was that what he was—just a friend? She looked at her cousin's happy face, noticing how all at once the petulant lines had been smoothed away, and a swift suspicion leapt into her mind. Had April known yesterday that Luis was back? Was that why she had wanted to go into Scarborough alone? And did that account for the air of excitement she'd worn—her unusual amiability?

April met her gaze, her blue eyes wide and guileless.

'You're getting a lovely tan, Lin, in fact you look loads better than you did when you first came here. Did you enjoy yourself yesterday? I'm sorry I had to ask our *bête noir* to collect you, but I couldn't think of anyone else who'd be able to do it.'

Lin drew a deep breath. Now for it. She said, a little too rapidly, 'Yes, it was marvellous. You know how much I love swimming, and the water was glorious, just like warm silk. Afterwards we had tea with Ruel and then——' She stopped, suddenly aware that April wasn't listening . . . wasn't even bothering to pretend that she was listening. She was scowling down at the letter she had just finished reading when Lin had come into her bedroom. It was from Godfrey—he wrote so frequently that Lin had come to recognize his thin, rather spidery handwriting.

She said, with a spurt of irritability, 'Godfrey's seen fit to take me to task for not writing to him often enough! He *knows* I hate writing letters—and

93

anyway, what is there to write about, living in a godforsaken hole like this?'

'It's a hole a great many people would enjoy very much, given the chance!' Lin retorted with unaccustomed asperity, and April gave a petulant shrug.

Lin, looking at her, suddenly discovered that she'd lost all desire to tell her about last night. She was so obviously uninterested in anything but her own affairs. And after all, what was there, really, to tell? A drive, a dinner, a dance . . . all in all it amounted to very little. And she hadn't been disloyal—except perhaps in her heart.

She said coolly, 'Well, there won't be any need for letters much longer, will there? Didn't you say that Godfrey was trying to get home in time for your birthday?

'Well, he isn't going to be able to manage that after all.' April's eyes sparkled with sudden excitement, her annoyance with Godfrey momentarily forgotten. 'Lin, about my birthday! I've had such a perfectly splendid idea! I'm going to throw a party, a really super one, here at Buonaventura. There are lots of people I'd like to ask. I want to make it a real bonanza—you know, a top band, fairy lights all over the grounds, flowers everywhere, champagne by the bucketful, marvellous food! Don't you think it sounds wonderful?'

'Why, yes—of course,' Lin said a little doubtfully.

April did not seem to notice her slight hesitation. 'I haven't thrown a *real* party since I married Godfrey—his idea of lavish entertainment is dinner for eight with bridge to follow!' She laughed excitedly. 'I'll really make Tobago sit up! Expense no object!'

'Well, let me know how I can help——' Lin began, but April interrupted her.

'Oh no! Darling, it won't be the kind of party *you're* used to planning! I shall have to see to it all myself, to make sure that every single thing is quite right, you know.' She hesitated. 'The only snag —I hope you won't mind too much—is that I shall probably have to leave you to your own devices a bit more than I have done. But you'll be able to amuse yourself, won't you? Go swimming with Mandy again and so on?'

Particularly so on, Lin thought with a tiny spurt of amusement as she followed her cousin down the wide polished staircase. Would April have been so ready to give her *carte blanche* if she'd known about last night? Well, she couldn't help feeling very glad now that she hadn't confessed! Apart from anything else, it would have been rather a pity to have done anything to spoil April's good mood! She sighed. If only she herself didn't have so many misgivings about the reason for it! However hard she tried, she could not manage to keep at bay the suspicions that had been knocking for admission ever since she'd heard April say that Luis was back. *Was* April's friendship with him as harmful as Ruel evidently supposed? Oh, of course it was the classic situation . . . elderly husband, young wife, handsome stranger, but surely April *wouldn't*?

The lunch with Luis on board his new yacht, *Starlight*, did not result in her feeling happier. She

95

and April drove into Scarborough just before midday and found Luis waiting for them on the quay.
He looked even more handsome than Lin remembered: immaculate in beautifully tailored slacks and
a snow-white shirt, and with smoked glasses hiding
his dark eyes.

He greeted Lin with friendly warmth, and April
with an easy familiarity which gave Lin an unpleasant jolt. He and April were so obviously on
the best of terms! She tried to force herself to be
rational. If his smile was admiring then surely that
was natural, for April looked radiant and beautiful
in a sheath dress which even to Lin's inexperienced
eyes shrieked Fifth Avenue, and with her golden
hair coiled round her head. Together, she and Luis
made a striking couple.

With an effort Lin concentrated her attention on
the yacht. She wasn't here to spy, she told herself
fiercely.

'Do you like it?' Luis asked her smilingly.

'It's beautiful.' It was. It was also the biggest
and most opulent-looking craft in the harbour. A
millionaire's plaything. *Was* Luis a millionaire and
if so, how? She must remember to ask April.

Luis seemed pleased. 'Wait till you see inside,'
he boasted, holding out his hands to help the two
girls aboard.

'It's a floating penthouse!' April exclaimed
enthusiastically.

It was not an exaggeration, but almost without
being aware of it Lin found herself comparing the
elegant decor and luxurious appointments with the
bareness of Ruel's bungalow. Fool! she adjured

herself angrily, and tried to enthuse as whole-heartedly as April.

Luis was an assiduous host, and the lunch was superb. April, sitting on a pile of jewel-bright cushions, her slender legs curled up beneath her, was obviously very much at home. Lin, listening to her gay laughter, watching her eager, animated face, wondered if she came alive like this for Godfrey. Undoubtedly she found Luis attractive . . . but then probably so would most women. What was it April had said about the little French girl whom Ruel had loved—' Of course she preferred Luis . . .'

No, Lin thought suddenly. There was no ' of course ' about it. Ruel lacked Luis' flamboyant good looks, his charm was far less obvious, but Ruel was worth two of Luis. The latter was just a little bit too sure of himself, just a bit too confident of his charm. He was, she suspected, a very vain man—but then so was April vain. They were very alike, those two.

She became suddenly aware that April was talking about the proposed party.

' Am I invited?' Luis asked, then added, with a somewhat rueful laugh, ' But I forgot. Of course you promised that charming stepson of yours you wouldn't invite me to Buonaventura, didn't you?'

April tossed him a glittering smile. ' What is it they say? Promises and pie-crust are made to be broken!' she said airily, and Luis laughed again.

Lin was staring at her. *Had* April promised that? She'd never said so before! She drew her brows together in a slightly puzzled frown. If that were true, then it explained why Ruel had behaved as he had the night she had arrived in Tobago . . . and why April had been so taken aback. But it didn't explain why April had given the promise in the first place! It wasn't in the least like her to do so!

Directly they got home she tackled her. 'April, why did you promise Ruel you wouldn't ask Luis to Buonaventura?'

Was it her imagination, or did April seem somewhat disconcerted? Certainly she avoided her cousin's eyes as she replied, 'Oh, my dear, it was ages ago! I've forgotten now. I expect he has, too.'

Lin did not believe her, but she knew from experience that it was was useless to persist. Instead she said slowly, 'You were joking, weren't you—when you said that to Luis about promises being made to be broken, I mean?'

April raised her brows. 'Why should I have been joking?'

The note in her voice made Lin flush. 'Because—' She stopped. It was no use conducting an argument with April along moral lines. She said quietly, 'I can understand the first time, because you were worried about me. But what will Ruel say if he finds out that you've invited Luis to the party?'

'I don't see why he should find out—at least, not until it's much too late to do anything about it!' April said carelessly. 'Anyway, as I've told you he's probably forgotten all about the hoo-ha. He's been keeping pretty quiet lately, thank goodness!'

'You won't send him an invitation?' Even as she felt her colour rise Lin could not resist asking the question.

'I will not! He wouldn't come, anyway, he's an anti-social creature. But I most certainly shall ask Luis, my little Puritan!'

Lin bit her lip, but April was already off on another tack.

'What are you going to wear? From what I've seen of the clothes you've brought with you you've got nothing suitable.' She frowned. 'I suppose I could lend you something of mine, even though I am a bit taller.'

Borrowed plumes . . . 'waiting for whatever crumbs may fall.' Ruel's sardonic words came vividly to Lin's mind and she said quickly, 'No, thank you, April. I—I think I'll probably try to buy some pretty material and make one.'

April shrugged. She knew that Lin was skilful with a needle and made a lot of her own clothes. If she chose to wear a home-made dress when everyone else would be wearing haute couture that was entirely up to her.

Lin waited until the end of the week and then caught a bus into Scarborough with the object of buying material and pattern for a frock. She had deliberately waited until April was too busy writing invitations to accompany her, for her resources were limited and she had no intention of being persuaded into buying something she simply could not afford.

In any case the bus journey proved to be an experience she would not readily have missed. She had become almost used to the astonishing variations of the Tobagan landscape, but travelling by bus she saw many tiny villages she had hitherto missed and gained a far better insight into the way in which the people lived and worked. What struck her most was the fact that everyone seemed to be as gay as larks: was it, she wondered, the perennial sunshine responsible for the beaming faces she saw everywhere?

Most of the seats on the bus were occupied by countrywomen who talked, argued and laughed among themselves, waved to everybody they passed on the road and generally treated the bus as if it was their own chauffeur-driven limousine instead of a public vehicle. People seemed to get on and off whenever they felt like it, so what with the frequent stoppages, and the fact that the route taken was so winding and tortuous, it was a good two hours before Lin finally arrived in Scarborough.

She had the sense carefully to avoid the shops frequented by April, where prices were sky-high, but instead hunted happily about in the smaller shops until at last she found something which was both pretty and reasonably inexpensive. It was a length of filmy, cobwebby stuff, shot with gossamer silver threads, and it was exactly the shade of green which Nicholas had once told her suited her better than anything else.

Outside the shop, blinking in the strong sunlight, she glanced at her watch. Half an hour to spare before she was due to catch the bus home. She thought rapidly. She'd rather like to take a look at the Botanical Gardens, but her first and most crying need was a long, cool drink. She had not taken more than half a dozen paces towards a small shop-cum-bar when a brown velvet voice at her elbow made her jump.

'Lin! What an unexpected pleasure!'

She turned quickly, to find Luis Cortes smiling down at her, his strong, even teeth dazzling white against the brown of his face.

'Why, hello.' She spoke awkwardly, but if he noticed her lack of enthusiasm he did not show it.

'Are you alone? Or is April here, too?'

'No. She's busy this morning. I—I came in by bus to buy some material for a dress.'

'By bus?' Luis' eyebrows rose. 'My *dear* girl! What a shattering experience!'

'It wasn't. It was fun.' Lin spoke truthfully, but Luis laughed rather as if she had made a good joke.

'You English have such phlegm!' He glanced at his handsome gold wristwatch. 'I do wish I could offer to run you back to Buonaventura, but unfortunately I have a business engagement in half an hour's time. But at least you will allow me to buy you a drink?'

'No—really——'

'But I insist.' Luis' hand was on her elbow, firmly propelling her towards the bar. Lin, making the best of a bad job, allowed him to buy her a fizzy lemonade. She really *was* parched, she simply couldn't wait any longer.

Luis' dark eyes smiled at her across the table. He did not seem to be in the least surprised by her constraint. Perhaps, she thought suddenly, he misconstrued it as shyness. Certainly it would never occur to him that his attentions could be anything but welcome. Suddenly, for the first time, she found herself disliking him very much and it had nothing to do with either Ruel or April. He simply was so damnably sure of himself and his power over women . . . so formidably handsome that doubtless he had become accustomed to easy conquests. And she had thought Ruel arrogant!

He was smiling, and she caught the glint of genuine amusement in his eyes, below the insolent lids.

'You are looking very lovely today, Lin.' (Heavens, did he think she was sitting there waiting for compliments?) 'I only wish I had more time to devote to your entertainment.' He gave her a slow, intimate smile which she was quite sure was calculated to make her heart beat that little bit faster. 'I am tempted—yes, I am strongly tempted—to break that appointment.'

'Oh, but—but you mustn't!' She saw Luis' brows rise again and added hastily, 'Business before pleasure! What *is* your business, Luis?'

There was a tiny silence, hardly noticeable, before Luis answered. 'Oh, I dabble a little, in this and that. Mostly stocks and shares,' he said smoothly— a little too smoothly. Then, with just the right amount of regret in his voice he added, 'But I am afraid you are quite right—about putting business before pleasure, I mean. I shall look forward to enjoying more of your company soon, however— *very* soon.'

Stars above, surely he didn't intend to add her to his list of conquests? The thought made the colour rush to Lin's face and she jumped to her feet in genuine confusion.

'My—my bus! I shall have to go now, Luis. If I miss it there won't be another one for ages!'

He seemed amused by the tremor in her voice, but much to her relief made no effort to detain her. He accompanied her out on to the street, talking still in his clear, rapid voice, charmingly, automatically, just as though he were wound up. When she said goodbye he stood for a moment smiling down at her, holding her hand for a shade too long despite her efforts to withdraw it.

'I hope you will find your journey back to Buonaventura—entertaining.' There was a teasing glint in the dark eyes. 'Take care of yourself' and then, as though it were an afterthought, 'Give my regards to April, won't you?' With a lift of the hand he was gone, leaving Lin staring after him, half annoyed, half amused.

What a coxcomb! she thought. Oh, surely there was no real need to worry about April? She hadn't always proved, in the past, to be the world's best judge of men, but what *was* there to commend Luis except his extraordinary good looks? Oh, and his money, of course. She found herself recalling his words. 'I dabble a little, in this and that . . .' Well, for a dabbler he seemed to have been quite astonishingly successful. Almost *too* successful, in such a very short time.

Frowning a little, she turned to cross the road, but before she could step forward a big car slid to a halt beside her. A Chevrolet. Absurdly, her heart began to race.

The door swung open. Ruel's voice said, 'May I have the pleasure of giving you a lift? To Buonaventura, I presume?'

He was alone in the car. Lin, her heart pounding, nodded assent and got in beside him without a word.

As the car moved off she stole a surreptitious glance at his profile. His face was set in the stern lines she knew so well, and her heart sank. Had he seen her with Luis? Not that it really mattered, except . . .

Unable to bear the tension any longer, she faltered, ' That *was* lucky. M-meeting you, I mean. I was going back by bus and it takes an age.'

' Didn't Cortes offer to take you home?'

So he *had* seen! Lin ran her tongue over suddenly dry lips, but before she could answer Ruel said, still in the same cold, uncompromising tone, ' I assume that you came into Scarborough this morning specifically to meet him?'

' Of course not!' Lin felt a tiny spurt of anger. How dare he assume any such thing? ' I—we met by chance.'

' I see.' His voice was ironic and Lin said defensively, ' But it *was*. I came into Scarborough to buy some dress material and—and I bumped into him outside the shop.'

' And so of course he insisted on inflicting his company on you?' Ruel was frowning at the road ahead, his eyes narrowed against the sun.

This was exactly what had happened, but she felt that he was hardly likely to believe her. Determined not to be provoked into another argument she bit her lip hard and kept silent.

He shot her a swift look, bleak and unsmiling. Then he said, ' You and he seem to be on very good terms, if I may say so.'

Whether he intended it or not, something in his voice made it sound like a careful insult. Lin's face flamed. Gone was all desire to conciliate.

Very clearly she said, 'No, you may not say so! You may think you've got the right to interfere in April's life, but I'm darned if I know what it's got to do with you what I do or who I meet!'

There was a long silence. When she dared to look at him again his face looked suddenly strangely haggard and Lin felt her heart contract. She was conscious of a wild, irrational desire to burst into tears, but then Ruel was speaking, every word like chipped ice.

'I stand corrected, but this time I am not going to apologize. You're not in Cortes' league, Lin. Don't play with fire.' He paused, then said heavily, 'Where's April? Don't tell me she sent you off with her blessing?'

Lin dug her finger nails into her palms. She said, carefully controlling her voice. 'She's busy, writing out invitations for the party.' She stopped short, realizing too late that since Ruel was not to receive an invitation the remark was somewhat tactless.

'Ah yes, the party.' A bleak little smile touched Ruel's lips and he took a corner about twice as fast as he should have done.

'I suppose you object to that, too?' Lin flung the question at him out of her abyss of misery. The man she loved was not this cold-eyed stranger but a man who had talked to her as one human being to another: who had laughed, and held her in her arms as they danced, and plucked frangipani for her hair and taught her the names of the stars that clustered the brilliant night sky.

' Not to the party. Just to what it's going to cost,' Ruel said grimly. Suddenly, without warning, he slammed on the brakes and the car jerked to a stop. He turned towards her.

' Lin, are you under the impression that my stepfather is a very wealthy man?'

Lin stared at him, the unexpectedness of the question leaving her startled and momentarily at a loss.

' Why, yes . . . of course. You said yourself that he was!'

' I think I used the word "reputedly".' Ruel's voice was grim. ' Oh, he's not a pauper, I'm not asking you to believe that. But he certainly isn't rich enough to be able to afford an extravaganza like the one that April is at present planning.' He felt her stiffen and held up his hand. ' There's nothing personal about this. I'm just stating facts. Have you any idea at all just how much money April has got through since she carried Godfrey ? She's like a child . . . an extravagant, wanton child. What she wants, she buys . . . and to hell with the expense.' He stopped. ' I'm telling you this for one reason. If she keeps on spending money like this there's going to be trouble . . . bad trouble. Godfrey's milking the estate dry in order to pamper to April's whims: he's spent capital he should never have touched. One bad season . . .'

Lin had gone white. What Ruel said carried conviction: she had been horrified herself by April's extravagance.

'But, Ruel, why doesn't Godfrey tell her the truth?'

'Because he wants to keep her happy, and that's the only way he knows how,' Ruel said curtly. 'God knows I've tried to talk sense to her. But she won't listen, starts having hysterics at the slightest suggestion that she should cut down. But if this lawsuit should go against Godfrey, as it very well may, I hate to think what is going to happen. At best, there's going to be a very unpleasant day of reckoning.'

'You mean . . . Godfrey will go bankrupt?' Lin's voice was a shaken whisper.

'Not if I can help it.' Ruel's face was bleak and hard. 'Apart from the fact that I'm fond of Godfrey, I won't let my sister be known as the daughter of a bankrupt.'

'But what can you do?'

'Not very much—now. If I'd come back sooner . . .' He shrugged wearily. 'What's the good of "ifs"?'

His voice was suddenly bitter. Lin thought: He's thinking about the girl he loved . . . if she had loved him instead of Luis. Something wrenched at her heart that might have been pity.

Perhaps he felt the quality of her silence for he turned his head and smiled faintly at her. His anger had gone.

'I'm sorry, Lin. I shouldn't have bothered you with all this. There's nothing you can do either.'

He paused and added wryly, 'It was your last remark that got under my skin. I'm not really a killjoy, you know.'

' I know.'   The words were scarcely audible.

He touched her cheek, very gently, and again he was the Ruel she loved.   ' With any luck Armageddon won't arrive.   Forget what I've said—and enjoy the party.'

Not if you're not going to be there, Lin thought as he re-started the car.   Her eyes were full of tears, but whether they were for Godfrey, desperately trying to buy love; or for April, with her distorted sense of values; or for Ruel, lonely and embittered; or for herself, the prisoner of dreams, she did not know.

CHAPTER VII

Lin tried hard to put her forebodings from her as the days—lovely, peaceful days—went by.   April was completely immersed in the preparations for her party, but although it was impossible for Lin, in the light of Ruel's disclosures, to view the lavish plans with anything but dismay, there was nothing she could do.   April was determined to make a splash, and all remonstrances fell on deaf ears.

Lin also strongly suspected that during her frequent absences in Scarborough April was seeing a lot of Luis Cortes, and it was small consolation to know that if so at least she was taking the trouble to be discreet.   She could not help wondering, uneasily, whether April too was playing with fire, but clung to the hope that her cousin was merely amusing herself. Surely Godfrey's return—which could not be long delayed, for he had written that the outcome of the lawsuit was expected very soon—would put an effective end to the friendship?

She was looking forward to meeting Godfrey, of whom everyone seemed to speak well. She had seen a photograph of him in Mandy's bedroom: a short, rather thickset man with a lined face and tired but kindly eyes. No trace there of good looks or even great charm—Mandy must take after her mother—but Lin felt instinctively that he was a man who could be trusted and a man who would always be kind. If ever April, comparing him with Luis Cortes, preferred the dross to the gold she would be unutterably foolish!

Since April was busy and, moreover, showed a marked disinclination for her company, Lin found herself spending a great deal more time with Mandy and Argos. Mandy would normally have been having lessons, but her governess was ill and she was making the most of an unexpected holiday. Together she and Lin spent many happy hours, swimming, surfing and exploring the island.

One day they visited Little Tobago, a tiny star-shaped island situated on the north-east corner of Tobago which had been made into a bird sanctuary, and which, Mandy said, was usually known as Bird of Paradise Island. Another day they went to the famous Buccoo Reef. Here they hired a glass-bottomed boat and Lin, staring down into the perfectly clear water, was surprised and entranced by the colours and formations of the beautiful sea gardens and fascinated by the friendliness of many of the jazzy-hued fish.

She found herself remembering Ruel's promise to

take her snorkeling. Evidently, she thought, he'd forgotten or else he was too busy. Or maybe, after their last disastrous encounter, he just didn't want to be bothered. Perhaps, if she were ever to cure herself of the foolish tendre she felt for him, it was just as well.

She said nothing to Mandy, but the following day, when they were walking down to a small bay within convenient reach of Buonaventura, Ruel, driving his white Chevrolet, overtook them.

The door was pushed open from inside. Ruel's voice, suddenly young and gay, said, ' Anyone want a lift to Arnos Vale?'

' Ruel!' In her excitement Mandy's voice was almost a squeal. ' I thought you'd forgotten! Have you taken the day off? Doesn't it matter?'

'I'm just playing truant for a few hours.' Ruel glanced at Lin as, bright-eyed and laughing, she scrambled with Argos into the back of the car. ' You've really never done any snorkeling before, have you, Lin?'

She shook her head and he laughed as the car moved forwards. ' Once you've been snorkeling you're hooked for life. There's nothing else to touch it. You put on your goggles, swim a few lazy strokes, and you find yourself in another world. It's unbelievable.'

It was. Lin, equipped with flippers and goggles, and with Ruel and Mandy gliding gracefully beside her, felt rather as though she were floating on the ceiling of a strange and marvellous room. Looking down, she saw a fairy-tale world of underwater canyons and ravines and spectacular coral reefs.

Moving clouds of rainbow-coloured fish swam slowly past her: bright blue fish, yellow and black fish, dark blue fish with diamond spots, even fish with transparent bodies.

Afterwards, as they lay side by side on the silvery sand, Ruel told her the names of the fish as she described them and related some of his experiences underwater. Mandy, who was never content to be still for long, was searching for sea-shells along the shore, Argos frisking at her heels.

Lin, listening in quiet content to the sound of Ruel's deep voice, thought he had never looked more relaxed or carefree. How brown he was! He was wearing only brief black bathing trunks and she realized, for the first time, the strength and power of his finely-made, hard-muscled body. An artist, yes, but a man of action as well . . .

She said dreamily, letting the soft warm sand trickle through her fingers, 'When I'm back in London, and it's snowing, and the buses are running an hour late and my nose is blue with cold, I shall always think about today.' She added wryly, 'Everyone should have an escape route, don't you think?'

Ruel sat up. He said harshly, almost violently, 'There's no such thing. That's what I thought my island was—a permanent escape route. But in the end you have to stop running away. You have to face up to reality, no matter how much it hurts.'

Lin, horrified by the effect of her words, saw the bitter lines etch themselves again deeply round his mouth. Her hands went out in an instinctive, half-appealing gesture.

'Ruel . . .'

His own hands shot out to clasp her wrists. His grip hurt, but she made no attempt to pull away.

For a moment they looked deep into each other's eyes. Then Ruel released her wrists and very gently cupped her face in his brown hands. He said, so softly that she could scarcely hear him, 'You're so sweet, Lin . . . sweet and genuine. I didn't think there was anyone like you left.' He smiled, and in the grey of his eyes there was a little steady flame. 'I once told you I'd rather paint places than people, didn't I? But I'd like to paint you . . . I wonder if I could ever get that crystalline quality of yours on to canvas?'

His dark head bent lower and Lin held her breath and waited for she knew not what. Then Mandy, shouting excitedly, came running to them across the sand and Ruel let her go, unhurriedly.

Her heart racing, Lin watched him bend over his small sister and exclaim admiringly over the shells that she proudly displayed. She held them all in her small brown hands—pink ones, yellow ones, mottled ones, streaked ones—and on her face was a look of rapt delight that was noticeably missing from her stepmother's when, later that day, it was her turn to show Lin a handful of bright stones.

'Godfrey's birthday present to me,' she said coolly. 'It's just arrived.'

Lin gave a gasp. It was a slender, dainty bracelet of sapphires, the colour of April's eyes.

'April! It's absolutely beautiful!' She looked up, uncertainly, into her cousin's unsmiling face. 'What's the matter? Don't you like it?'

April gave a short, half angry laugh. 'I might, if

I hadn't seen the jewels Mandy's mother used to wear! They're Mandy's now, worse luck. Here, I'll show you something!'

Lin watched wonderingly while she unlocked a small safe and pulled out a worn leather case. She pressed the catch with her thumb and the lid flew open to reveal a glittering diamond necklace.

Lin caught her breath, awed by the splendour of the jewels. ' Oh, it's marvellous!'

' Now do you see why I can't get wildly excited over a sapphire bracelet?' April asked disagreeably. ' This is worth a kingdom. I wanted a diamond necklace, too: Godfrey knew that I did!' She let the splendid, glittering thing run through her fingers, the expression on her lovely face frankly covetous.

' Put it away!' Lin begged, with an anxious glance at the window. ' April, aren't you afraid of burglars? Is it really safe to keep a necklace like that here?'

' Usually it's kept at the bank with some other jewellery. Godfrey only sent for it because he wanted to show it to Mandy on her last birthday. Then he got called away suddenly to New York and in the rush he didn't do anything about sending the necklace back.' Reluctantly she closed the lid. ' Isn't it maddening to think that such a heavenly thing belongs to a scruffy urchin like Mandy? She won't be able to wear it for years and years. I wanted to borrow it for gala occasions, but for once Godfrey put his foot down.' She laughed, without humour. ' I assume the bracelet is his odd idea of compensation!'

' Don't be ungrateful, April! It's a lovely bracelet and it will go beautifully with the dress you're wearing tomorrow,' Lin said quietly.

April shrugged. 'Diamonds would look better.' She lit a cigarette, puffing out a cloud of smoke before asking abruptly, 'What about the dress you're making? Have you finished it?'

'Nearly. It will be ready by tomorrow.' She had been working on it, each night in her room, until the small hours, thankful to have something to occupy her mind. When finally she put her needle down she was usually so weary that she went straight to sleep. Without such an anodyne, she thought ruefully, she would probably have tossed and turned until daybreak, thinking of Ruel—and to what purpose?

April said no more, but the next day, when she and Lin were dressing for the party, her face showed her surprise that her cousin had achieved such excellent results. The design was of necessity simple, but it suited her perfectly, and the colour was exactly right.

'Why, it's rather nice, Lin! For a home-made frock, that is!' she added, a little grudgingly. She was always chary of paying compliments to any member of her own sex.

Lin laughed. Since Ruel was not to be at the party she didn't particularly care whether the dress looked nice or not. April had promised, with unusual magnanimity, to introduce her to plenty of partners, but what did anyone else matter? There was no room in her mind or her heart for anyone but Ruel. Her cheeks were suddenly hot. She hadn't dared to let herself think too much about those few moments yesterday on the beach, when for once Ruel's defences seemed to have been down. She only knew, with a faint hope dawning in her heart, that he wasn't entirely indifferent towards her. There had been no mistaking the tenderness in his voice and eyes . . . or the fact that he had wanted to kiss her. ' You're so sweet . . . sweet and genuine.' His voice had lingered on that last word, almost as though he'd found it hard to believe. What had *she* been like, the girl he had loved and lost, first to Luis Cortes and then to the sea? For the first time she felt an intense desire to hear that tragic story from Ruel's own lips. She felt sure that there was more to it than April had told her. It was not merely thwarted pride that had turned a gay young man into a lonely recluse . . . and it was deep unhappiness that had driven those furrows down his lean cheeks and given his grey eyes such sombre shadowing.

She became suddenly aware that April was watching her with unusual intentness.

' You look different, Lin . . . and it isn't just that dress.' There was an almost speculative gleam in her blue eyes. ' If I didn't know better I'd say you were in love!'

Lin flushed guiltily. It wasn't like April to be so perceptive. She said lightly, ' It must be the atmosphere . . . Buonaventura *en fête*!—Your dress looks absolutely stunning, April.'

As she had hoped, April was easily distracted. ' Yes, isn't it?' she said ingenuously, giving a swift, satisfied look into the tall mirror that flanked the bathroom door. ' Mind you, I wouldn't like to tell you how much it cost!'

'And I don't think I'd like to know,' Lin thought as she turned away to brush her hair. April had certainly meant it when she'd said no expense was to be spared. The house was a mass of flowers—rainbow-coloured bougainvillea, golden allamandas, flaming ixoras, scarlet hibiscus and many other exotic blooms which she did not recognize—while fairy lights and Chinese lanterns decorated the grounds. Crate after crate of champagne had been delivered, an outside firm of caterers had been engaged to help Aunt Lou with the refreshments and the band, April said, was the best in the Caribbean. What was it Ruel had said? . . . 'A day of reckoning . . .'

Lin's face was very sober as she applied a light dusting of powder and a trace of soft coral lipstick . . . all the make-up she ever used. When she had finished she looked critically at her reflection, wondering just what it was April had seen in her face that betrayed her secret. To her own eyes she looked exactly the same—oh, except that her skin had tanned to a smooth golden-brown, her cheeks had filled out a little and the dark shadows had disappeared from beneath her eyes. Her lips curved into a rueful smile. Perhaps it was a good thing that Ruel would not be at the party. She might not be able to hide her happiness at seeing him . . . and then the fat *would* be in the fire!

She heard the strains of music and decided, reluctantly, that it was time she went downstairs. She sighed. She *hated* parties . . . always had done. And this one was likely to be worse than most.

On the landing she hesitated. Mandy was already

in bed, but it was unlikely that she was asleep. With a soft rustle of skirts she ran swiftly down the corridor and tapped on the child's bedroom door, which was ajar. The room was in darkness, but Mandy was awake, for her voice came immediately.

' Who is that?'

' Me—Lin. I thought you might like to see my dress.' Lin switched on the light and crossed over to the small white bed. To her surprise Mandy was sitting bolt upright, propped against the pillows.

' What's the matter? Is the music keeping you awake?'

Mandy shook her head. In her skimpy cotton nightdress she looked oddly frail and defenceless. ' Not the music. I—I've got a bit of toothache.'

' Oh, how horrid!' Lin was all sympathy. ' How long have you had it? Shall I fetch you an aspirin?'

' Oh, yes, please!' Mandy looked relieved. ' It isn't *very* bad, you know, but it niggles.'

' Well, it's likely to get worse unless you have the tooth seen to,' Lin told her austerely. ' Who's your dentist?'

Mandy wriggled. ' I don't like going to the dentist.'

' Then you're a little noodle,' Lin scolded, fetching her the aspirin. Privately she made up her mind to have a word with Ruel. If anyone could get Mandy to the dentist it would be him. It would certainly be no use referring the matter to April, even though the responsibility was actually hers.

Mandy's big eyes were taking in every detail of Lin's appearance. ' You look awfully pretty, Lin—

much prettier than April, even.'

Lin laughed. 'Flatterer! You haven't seen April tonight. She looks wonderful!'

'Is she wearing my diamonds?' The question came point-blank and took Lin completely by surprise.

'Your——? Of course not! She's wearing the pretty bracelet your father sent her for her birthday.'

'I just wondered. I've got a lovely diamond necklace, did you know? It—it was my mother's, and she left it to me when she died. April thinks she ought to have diamonds, too: I heard her tell Daddy so.'

'Well, I expect he *will* give her a necklace one day,' Lin said cheerfully.

'Why should he? He didn't give my mother hers.' Mandy must have seen the startled expression on Lin's face, for she added, 'He didn't, really. Ruel's father gave it to her. Ruel told me.'

Lin was silent. She hadn't realized that Ruel's father had been wealthy, though of course there was no earthly reason why he shouldn't have been. She opened her mouth, then shut it again. It wasn't fair to ask Mandy questions, and in any case the fortunes of the Saxon family were absolutely none of her business.

Mandy looked up at her. 'Lin?'

'Yes?'

'Are you cross because I said that about April wanting to wear my diamonds?'

Lin came to with a start. 'Of course I'm not cross. Mandy, don't you think you ought to lie down and try to go to sleep now? The aspirin will start to work pretty soon, I expect.'

Mandy lay down obediently, but kept her eyes fixed on Lin's face. 'I—I suppose you wouldn't read me a story before you go downstairs?'

Lin laughed but acquiesced, secretly glad of the excuse to linger. By the time she had read Mandy a fairy story and tucked her up for the night, the party sounded as though it was well under way. She went hesitantly down the stairs, wishing that the house didn't seem to be quite so full of people, all laughing, talking and drinking—especially drinking. There was a momentary lull in the music and she could hear the popping of corks even above the gay chatter.

For a moment she stood irresolute, seized by the paralysing shyness that always afflicted her at parties of this sort, then looked around for April. She was nowhere to be seen among the crowd gathered round the bar and buffet: she must be dancing. Resignedly she made her way through the throng to the drawing room, tonight converted into a ballroom, and stood by the doorway, watching.

She saw April almost immediately. A slender snow-maiden, in her white dress, a wreath of white flowers in the shining masses of her hair, and, apart from Godfrey's bracelet, no touch of colour about her except that which was supplied by her own vivid colouring. She was dancing very close to her tall, dark-haired partner, looking up into his face through her long gold-tipped lashes and laughing. It was Luis.

Lin felt her heart miss a beat. She had hoped against hope that in the end April would decide against asking Luis to the party. She did not believe for one moment that Ruel's attitude had changed, or that he had forgotten the promise April had made him. She might like to pretend that the ' hoo-ha ', as she'd called it, was all over, but Lin, remembering his anger the day he had seen her and Luis together in Scarborough, felt sure that this was not the case. In breaking her promise and inviting Luis to Buonaventura April was simply asking for trouble.

' Striking couple, aren't they?' A red-headed girl Lin did not know spoke at her elbow, her eyes, like Lin's, fixed on April and Luis.

' Yes.' Lin forced herself to answer, if briefly. They *were* a striking-looking couple, the one so fair, the other so dark . . . and they danced beautifully together. Nobody else on the floor could hold a candle to them.

' While the cat's away . . .' the girl said, and laughed, a horrid, knowing little laugh that made Lin's skin prickle. The colour flooded her face, but before she could answer the music had stopped and the girl had turned away.

April, flushed and sparkling, caught sight of Lin and broke away from Luis' encircling arm.

' Darling, where *have* you been? Skulking in a corner?' She gave a breathless little laugh. ' I promised to introduce you to some nice young men, didn't I?' She glanced vaguely round the room. ' Nigel, come and meet my cousin. Where *is* the man? Damn, he must have bolted to the bar. He's hopeless. Greg, get Lin a drink!'

And her duty done by Lin, she was gone, back

to Luis' arms as the music started once more. Lin stared after her, trying not to let her disquiet show on her face.

'Hey, I think we're supposed to be getting acquainted, aren't we?' said a plaintive, somewhat adenoidal voice, and Lin, wrenching her attention away from April, found herself looking into a pair of myopic-looking brown eyes. Greg turned out to be a solemn young man addicted to modern poetry and modern art. His attempt to engage Lin in deeply intellectual conversation failed miserably—inevitably, since her favourite poet was Tennyson and she liked a tree to look like a tree—but since he was delighted to find a seemingly attentive audience, and a very pretty one to boot, he felt not the slightest desire to seek pastures new.

All the time Greg was earnestly propounding his views on surrealist art Lin was aware of April without actually watching her. Seemingly tireless, she danced with other partners, but always came back to Luis. People were noticing . . . she could almost hear the whispers. Didn't April care any more what people thought?

The music brought her and Luis to within a few inches of where she and Greg were standing. April's left arm was tight round Luis' neck and she was smiling provocatively up at him. Looking over her buttercup head, Luis' eyes met Lin's. She saw the black brows lift sharply, as though he had read her thoughts, and then his mouth twitched into an amused smile. It was more than she could stand. With a muttered apology she interrupted Greg mid-sentence and fled out on to the loggia, the music following her through the windows. She stood quite still, staring blindly out into the garden, almost unaware of time or place, until a voice behind her made her spin round like a startled fawn.

'Lin!' It was Luis facing her, a smiling Luis. The smile on the face of a tiger . . . only that was too silly, because Luis wasn't a tiger.

He came towards Lin. 'I saw the expression on your face when I was dancing with April. You looked most disapproving.' He laughed softly. 'Dare I ask why?'

Lin looked him in the eye, a straight, fearless look. 'Do you really have to ask why?'

He laughed again. 'Feeling neglected?' He was so close now that their shoulders were almost touching.

'Neglected?' Lin's thoughts whirled. Heavens, Luis surely didn't think—*couldn't* think—that she was jealous?

'I don't think——' she began indignantly, but got no further. There was a faint noise, like a twig snapping underfoot, and Luis took one quick look into the shadows. Then she heard him suck in his breath. Suddenly, bewilderingly, his arms went round her and she was crushed in a suffocating embrace, his lips silencing her instinctive protest. For a moment she was too stunned to struggle. She stood absolutely still and rigid for what seemed an age, a dreadful, crawling age, thinking, ' This *can't* be happening . . . it can't!' and then a deep voice, achingly familiar, said quietly, expressionlessly, 'I think that's quite enough, Cortes. Lin, will you go inside, please?'

Ruel stepped out of the shadows. Even in the dim light she saw that his face was white to the lips. And his eyes . . . she thought afterwards that if ever a man looked murder at anyone, Ruel Saxon looked it then at Luis Cortes.

Her first feeling was of utter relief. She wrenched herself from Luis' arms and almost ran towards the tall, motionless figure, making no effort to keep the thankfulness out of her voice as she said ' Ruel . . .' Then she stopped, frightened by the grimness of his face. Why was he looking at *her* like that?

' Go inside, Lin.' She had heard that note in his voice before.

Luis said, ' Yes, Lin darling, go inside,' but it did not even register. She was looking at Ruel, and at what she read in his face she gave a strangled gasp. Then she turned and fled, back through the brilliantly lit ballroom, up the stairs and into the sanctuary of her own bedroom, leaving Ruel and Luis facing each other alone in the shadows.

Trembling all over, she flung herself down on the bed and buried her head in her arms. How long had Ruel been standing there? Surely he had seen exactly what happened? He must have realized that she had been kissed against her will . . . he *couldn't* have believed that she had surrendered willingly to Luis' embrace! She remembered the expression on his face and gave what was almost a sob of despair. He *had* believed just that. It was no good trying to deceive herself.

She lay on her bed for a long time, until at last she realized that the house had become still and silent. The party must be over. She got up, feeling strangely stiff and cold. She wondered drearily what had happened between Ruel and Luis after she'd gone. Had they resorted to violence, or did that kind of thing only happen on the movies and in books? In any case she wasn't afraid for Ruel: he was more than a match for Luis. And Luis deserved all he got! She was shaken by sudden anger. What on earth had possessed him to pounce on her like that? There'd been no passion in his kiss . . . it had been more like a cold-blooded exercise! She was almost sure that he hadn't followed her out on to the loggia in order to make love to her, just as she was almost sure that April had sent him. April! She caught her breath. What had happened to April?

As if in answer to her question there was a soft tap on her door and it opened. April stood there, looking tired but oddly triumphant.

Lin sprang towards her. ' April . . .?' There was a world of anxiety in her voice.

' Don't worry, goose! Everything's all right.' April, flung herself down on the bed, careless of her lovely dress. ' No corpses, no nothing! Not even bloodstains on the loggia!' She laughed, and there was no doubt that she was genuinely amused. ' I suppose you know you saved the day, coz? You and some quick thinking by Luis.'

Lin stared. ' I—what do you mean, April?'

April leant back, her lovely rounded arms behind her head. She looked at Lin in faint astonishment. ' Darling, do I really have to spell it out? You know what happened as well as I do! Contrary to my expectations dear Ruel came snooping round the house. I didn't think he'd bother or I wouldn't have invited Luis—yes, I know I told you it didn't matter, but I knew all the time that there'd be hell to pay if he found Luis here.' She yawned. 'And so there would have been, only luckily Luis spotted him first and had the presence of mind to make a pass at you.'

For a moment Lin could not believe her ears. ' You mean—he did that just because he knew Ruel was watching?' Her face was white and tense with anger and in spite of herself her voice shook.

' Why else? Darling, you must know you're not Luis' type!' There was a slight edge to April's tone. ' The whole point was that when he told Ruel that *you* had invited him to the party, and not me, Ruel didn't have too much difficulty in believing him. After what he'd just seen . . .' She laughed, then added, almost indifferently, ' I believe they had one helluva row just the same, but since I wasn't involved . . . She left the sentence unfinished.

' Luis told Ruel that *I* had invited him here tonight? But—April! That's a downright lie!' Lin's eyes were flashing, her whole body taut with outraged protest. ' I won't be a party to lies! You've got to tell Ruel the truth!'

It was April's turn to stare. ' I? My dear girl, don't be an idiot! Of course I shan't tell him the truth! He'd be furious!'

Lin was feeling sick and shaken. Her voice trembling, she said, ' Doesn't it occur to you that I might tell Ruel the truth myself?' She stopped, desperately afraid that she was going to cry.

April's beautiful face was suddenly hard and her eyes had narrowed. ' What are you talking about,

Lin? Why all the fuss? Why should you care whether Ruel thinks you invited Luis here tonight or not? You're a free agent . . . I'm not, worse luck! What does one little lie matter?' She paused, then added plaintively, ' I'd have thought you'd have been only too glad to get me out of a nasty hole!'

' Which you dug for yourself!' Lin said with unwonted sharpness. She suddenly felt very tired, not only physically but emotionally. She looked at her cousin and for the first time in her life saw her as she really was—utterly selfish, utterly self-centred. Ann was right. The only trouble was, she thought desolately, that the scales had fallen from her eyes just a little too late. After tonight, how could she expect Ruel to believe that she couldn't care less about Luis Cortes?

CHAPTER VIII

The next day brought Lin a letter from Ann. Momentarily, at least, it took her mind off her problems, for it was full of the plans she and Charles were making for their quiet register office wedding and their subsequent move ' up North '. They had been lucky enough to find a large unfurnished flat on the outskirts of Leeds at an unbelievably low rent: at the moment, Ann wrote, it was all chocolate brown paint and khaki-coloured wallpaper, but they were hoping to redecorate it themselves and make it look presentable.

' By the time you come back to England we should

be all shipshape and Bristol fashion,' Ann wrote. 'You will come and stay with us for a few days, won't you, until you've got yourself sorted out? Why not find a job in Leeds? It really isn't a bad city, and it's not as if you're keen on " swinging " London.' The letter ended with a teasing postscript. ' Found that dreamboat we talked about yet? Remember I'm keeping my fingers crossed for you!'

Lin's face was wistful as she folded the letter and put it back in its envelope. Reserved, self-contained Ann sounded so happy . . . so radiantly happy! Getting married must be wonderful . . . if it was to the right man. No wonder Ann could write so light-heartedly about dingy paint and dreary wallpaper: she was seeing life through rose-coloured spectacles. But without them . . . ? She gave an involuntary shiver . A grey northern city after the blue Caribbean? Oh, she ought not to feel like that . . . it was stupid, ungrateful. And it wasn't even logical. It wasn't the palm trees and the sun-kissed sea and the silver beaches she'd miss. She'd live underground and think it was Paradise if only Ruel was with her.

She thought of Ann's postscript. Would Ann think that Ruel qualified for the description of ' dreamboat '? Probably . . . he was good-looking enough. But she loved him or so much more than his looks. She loved the queer, embittered, maddeningly attractive man for himself: with all his faults, his moods, his difficult ' corners '. And she had an intense longing to make him happy, to smooth away the harsh and bitter lines from his face, to make him forget the tragedy of the past.

Her thoughts were like a roundabout, they always

came back to the same point. How would Ruel react
the next time she saw him? There'd been more than
anger in his face last night—when he'd first looked
at her there had been a flash of hurt, incredulous
disappointment as well. Undoubtedly he had
thought the worst—and who could blame him?
There'd been nothing half-hearted about Luis' embrace! If only she had had time to struggle . . . cry
out! Another moment and she would have recovered
from the shock, wrenched herself free and hit Luis
across his self-satisfied, smiling mouth!

Her lips folded tightly together. Perhaps she was
wrong . . . perhaps Ruel didn't care at all. All the
same, at the first opportunity she meant to tell him
the whole truth about last night, whether he believed
it or not. Well, nearly the whole truth. Even now,
despite her resentment at the way in which she had
been used, she knew she wouldn't be able to give
April away. Old habits die hard, and that particular
habit . . . shielding and defending April from the
results of her folly . . . was well ingrained.

April herself didn't seem to be suffering from any
pangs of remorse. She slept until well after midday
and came down as fresh and as sparkling as if she
had not danced half the night away. She did not
seem to notice her cousin's pale cheeks and heavily
shadowed eyes, and for this Lin was thankful. The
last thing she wanted was for April to guess the way
she felt about Ruel and she knew that she had
already come within an ace of giving herself away.

Since April had always possessed the enviable
faculty of being able to eradicate unpleasant things
from her memory, whatever constraint there was was

on Lin's side and not on hers. Nevertheless there were several awkward pauses in their conversation, and it was to bridge one of these that Lin showed her Ann's letter.

April scanned it in silence, then handed it back to Lin with a laugh which jarred unpleasantly.

'Poor old Ann! Doesn't it sound unutterably dreary—an unfurnished flat in Leeds? *What* a fate! Still, I don't suppose she could expect much more— she isn't exactly the type to set the world on fire, is she?'

Lin flushed and answered hotly, 'I think she sounds very happy. Charles is lucky: she'll make him a marvellous wife!'

There was a sudden gleam in April's blue eyes. 'Is that another dig at me, coz?'

Her lips parted in an amused smile as Lin did not answer. She had said all she had to say last night, during the first really bitter quarrel they had ever had. There was nothing further to add.

After a moment or two April shrugged. There was, Lin thought, a slight touch of bravado about the gesture.

'Not to worry. Godfrey will be home soon and then you'll be able to enjoy watching me play the part of a devoted and adoring wife!'

'I shan't stay after Godfrey gets home.' Lin spoke very quietly. It was idle to dream . . . to build castles in the air. Miracles didn't really happen, at least not to people like her. The sooner she thought about picking up the threads of her old life again the better.

April's eyes widened. 'But why? You're enjoying yourself here, aren't you? I meant you to stay until after Christmas!'

'For companionship?' Lin asked drily, and April had the grace to flush.

'Well, I admit that we haven't spent a lot of time together just lately, but I did warn you that I'd be tied up with the party!—It was a good party, wasn't it?' she added naively.

'Very,' Lin answered, as drily as before.

April shot her a dubious glance. 'Oh, Lin, stop looking so glum! I suppose you're still worrying about last night?'

'I'm worried most about you,' Lin said unsteadily. She paused for a moment, then went on pleadingly, 'April, won't you please stop seeing Luis? People were talking about you last night, you know. Even if—even if Ruel doesn't say anything to Godfrey it's possible that he might hear—rumours. He—he looks so nice. Don't hurt him!'

For a moment April was silent. Then she smiled, the warm enchanting smile that Lin liked to think was the real April.

'Darling, there's no need to worry! For one thing Godfrey won't pay any attention to rumours and for another Luis really is perfectly harmless. For heaven's sake don't *you* start getting a thing about him! Oh, I know he treated you rather badly last night, but that was for my sake—he'll apologize when next he sees you.' She paused, and then as Lin said nothing added coaxingly, 'Look—he's invited me to a party aboard his yacht tomorrow night. If it'll make you feel any better I'll ask him to invite you, too. Just to make up for what happened.'

'No!' The word burst from Lin's lips. She never wanted to see Luis Cortes again. 'Oh, April, don't go!'

April's face set in stubborn, sullen lines.

'You're being very difficult, Lin,' she said coldly. She flicked an imaginary speck of dust from her sleeve. 'I'm going for a drive. Coming?'

Lin shook her head and with a shrug April went off by herself. Lin stared after her, her eyes wide and unhappy. If only she could believe that Luis was perfectly harmless! What was it Ruel had said —'My objections to Luis Cortes are based on far more than prejudice'? She frowned to herself. She wished she knew how Ruel had managed to get April to promise him that she would not ask Luis to Buonaventura. Surely she wouldn't have done so unless . . . unless . . .

Restlessly she pushed the ugly thought away from her and rose to her feet. The minutes seemed to be ticking by with agonizing slowness, but that was only because she was longing for Ruel to come home. She felt that she could hardly wait to see him . . . to explain about Luis, and yet at the same time she was trembling inwardly with apprehension. If he was in one of his black moods . . .

She glanced at her wristwatch. Nearly three o'clock. It might have been better if she'd gone for a drive with April after all. It was a pity Mandy wasn't available . . . her governess had come back and they were making up for lost lesson time. Mandy wasn't very pleased about that! Lin smiled to herself, remembering the little girl's agonized expression when she had seen Miss Purley coming up the drive first thing that morning. Poor Mandy! She hated lessons as much as she seemed to hate going to the dentist. Luckily her toothache was better now, but Lin had warned her that it would only be a temporary reprieve—she'd have to have the tooth filled sooner or later.

Wearily she pushed her damp hair back from her brow. She supposed the most sensible thing to do would be to go into the house and read a book, but she also knew that she was too much on edge to concentrate. Perhaps she would walk down to the bay and have a leisurely swim. Then she hesitated, frowning in annoyance. She would need her sunglasses. She had been wearing them the day before yesterday, when she and Mandy had been walking down to the beach (was it really only that short time ago that she and Ruel had swum together in that marvellous clear water at Arnos Vale? It felt like aeons ago . . .). Afterwards, when she and Mandy had been playing with a beach ball, Ruel had stuffed them into his pocket for safety. As he hadn't returned them presumably they were in his bungalow. Would he mind if she went in and looked for them? She'd probably get a headache if she went for a walk in this glaring sun without some protection for her eyes.

She tapped softly on the door of the bungalow, but as she had expected there was no answer. She peeped through the window and immediately saw what she had come for, lying on a small table with some books and magazines. For a moment she hesitated, then she tried the door. It was not locked. Trying hard not to feel so much like an intruder, she went in, grabbed her sunglasses and was on her way out when she noticed the easel—and the canvas on it. The shock was so great that she almost gasped aloud. It was her own face looking at her . . . to her eyes like and yet strangely unlike. Bewildered, her heart racing, she went closer and stood looking at it. When had Ruel done this? He had drawn with tenderness and perception all that was individual in the face— the delicately moulded bones, the sweetness of the mouth, the wistfulness of the expression—and the result was as memorable as his portrait of Mandy. Lin suddenly found herself trembling. Ruel had given her beauty—a beauty she did not think she possessed.

She was so absorbed that she did not hear the sound of approaching footsteps. It was some instinct, some inborn intuition, that made her whirl round with a sudden horrible prescience of what she was going to see. Ruel was standing in the doorway.

Lin's face went crimson. She said, stammering badly, ' I-I c-came to fetch my s-sunglasses.'

Ruel's face was as remote and as expressionless as that of an Egyptian pharoah. He said politely, ' I see you found them.' His eyes went past her to the portrait on the easel. ' Do you like it?' He might, she thought, have been asking the question of a complete stranger.

She swallowed hard. ' How——?'

She could not finish the sentence, but he guessed what she meant. ' Not from memory. I made a preliminary sketch one day when you were sitting in the garden with Mandy. You didn't see me.' He paused. 'It isn't finished, of course.' Nor will it be. The words, unspoken, hung between them as deliberately he removed the portrait from the easel. He held it for a moment in his hands, looking from it to her, and she thought that he seemed to be making some mental comparison. Then he put it down, and she saw him brush his hands across his eyes.

She said, with difficulty, 'I'm sorry. I shouldn't have come in, should I?'

He shrugged without answering and she said bitterly, 'You make me feel like a trespasser.'

'That is exactly how I felt last night.' Ruel's voice was suddenly harsh, and Lin winced. She said breathlessly, 'Ruel, I know what you must think, but it wasn't like that at all. I want to tell you. Luis——'

He interrupted her, his face bleak with bitter pride. 'You needn't explain. As you once saw fit to remind me, it has nothing to do with me what you do.' He gave a mirthless laugh. 'Now if I were your husband . . . ' He paused significantly.

'Yes?'

'I'd beat you,' he said coolly.

Lin's hands clenched. 'Really? You seem to have a strange idea of the function of civilized husbands!' Was that hard, brittle voice really hers?

His lip curled. 'I was forgetting. I suppose it's a family tradition that husbands exist merely for the purpose of writing nice fat cheques.'

'Oh!' Lin caught her breath. What was the use? Blindly she moved forward, only to find Ruel barring her way. He looked down at her, his eyes suddenly glittering.

'I once warned you against playing with fire, Lin. I suppose it never occurred to you that in coming here this afternoon—alone—you might get yourself badly burned?'

She felt suddenly afraid. 'Ruel, let me go, please!'

'Not yet?' he said savagely. 'Not till I've taught you a lesson!' He pulled her roughly towards him and his mouth came down hard on hers. The kiss seemed to last for ever. It was a passionate kiss—there was nothing remotely clinical about Ruel's lovemaking—but Lin, sensing the man's bitterness, anger and frustration, was aware of an intense desolation. She felt the tears welling up in her eyes and when at last he released her she felt them spill over and begin to run down her cheeks. She could not see his face through them, and so she did not see his expression change.

'Lin, you're crying . . . ah, darling, don't cry!'

His hands were on her again. This time they were curiously gentle, but she tore herself away, dashing the tears from her eyes with the back of her hand.

'If I'm crying it's for you, Ruel—you and your blindness! You've lived with hate and bitterness for so long that you're all warped and twisted!' She choked. 'You can't see straight any more! You—you can't even recognize love when you see it!'

'My God,' said Ruel in a queer, shaken voice, but Lin hardly heard him. To her anger now was added shame. What on *earth* had made her say that? How *could* she have been so lacking in pride? With a despairing sob, her eyes again blinded by tears, she fled past him and darted out into the brilliant sunshine. Her legs felt as though they were not her own, but that did not impede her flight. She heard him call out after her, but she did not stop, until halfway along the narrow path she collided violently with someone whom she discovered to be Joseph.

Ruel was behind her. His hand was actually on her arm when she heard Joseph say, with unusual urgency, ' Massah Ruel, this came for you,' and saw that he was holding out what appeared to be a cablegram. Something leapt into Ruel's eyes which might, or might not, have been apprehension and momentarily his grip slackened. It was all the opportunity she needed. Careless of dignity or discretion, she had jerked herself free and was tearing across the lawn to where she had seen, out of the corner of her eye, Mandy's governess about to leave Buonaventura in her small car.

' Miss Purley, please will you give me a lift? To— to Guacho Bay?' Ruel wouldn't know where she intended to go, she thought wildly, he would hardly follow! Looking back over her shoulder, she saw that he and Joseph were still standing where she had left them. For a moment it struck her that there was something curiously rigid about Ruel's tall figure, then she dismissed the idea as fancy. Perhaps the next time she saw him she would have her stupid emotions better under control!

If Miss Purley was surprised by her request—and by her appearance—she did not show it. She was an elderly, pleasant-faced woman who had taught school in Birmingham for thirty-seven years and whose dream had been to spend the years of her retirement somewhere in the sun. She was glad, she told Lin, of the chance to earn a little extra money to eke out her small pension, though she ruefully admitted that her small pupil posed something of a problem.

'This is one of her favourite spots, isn't it?' she asked Lin as they reached the bay. 'Perhaps she'll join you in a little while. She was out of the room like a shot when I announced that lessons were over for today!'

Lin hoped not. Much as she liked Mandy, just at present she badly wanted to be alone. For a long time she lay face down on the silvery sand, thinking hard, and it was as though her stormy heart was lulled by the rushing of the breakers on the coral reef. It was so peaceful that she stayed there longer than she had actually intended, rousing herself only when she found that the sun had gone down. She hurried then, but despite her haste it was nearly dark when she finally arrived home at Buonaventura.

Aunt Lou met her at the door. To her horror Lin saw that her eyes were red-rimmed and her usually cheery, smiling face was streaked with tears.

'Oh, Missy Lin, do you know where the missus is?'

Lin stared at her. 'April? Why, no. She went for a drive early this afternoon. What's the matter? *Not Mandy?*' Her voice was suddenly sharp with alarm.

'No, missy. It's Massah—Massah Selby. He's been taken bad.' Aunt Lou gave a doleful sob as Lin, remembering the cablegram she had seen Joseph give to Ruel, exclaimed in dismay.

'This is for you—Massah Ruel left it.' She waddled away, weeping noisily, while Lin, suddenly white-faced, tore open with trembling fingers the envelope she had just been given.

The letter it contained was short and looked as though it had been written in a desperate hurry. It read:

My dear,

I seem to spend my time apologizing to you when it is probably patently obvious that I'd prefer to be doing something else. Forgive me for the devil that rides me: jealousy is love's curse, though that is no excuse for what I said and did. You are right about my not seeing straight. To go away now without first making my peace with you would be unthinkable under any circumstances but these—Godfrey was taken very ill on his way home from New York and is at present in hospital in Antigua. I must go to him at once. I can't find April to tell her, but I expect she will want to join us. Help her all you can. Until I come back—I trust you, Lin. Yours, Ruel.

Jealousy is love's curse . . . She read the words, but did not dare to dwell on them or to conjecture what they meant. She was beset by fear for Godfrey . . . concern for April. How ill was 'very ill'? Oh, surely he wasn't going to die! And April . . . where *was* April? She ought to know at once . . . she'd want to catch the first possible plane to New York! Lin pressed her hands to her head. Oh, if only she knew where she'd gone . . . could get in touch with her! There was no telling when she'd get back!

In her absence there was no time to brood. Aunt Lou and Joseph, who were obviously devoted to their master, were simply shattered by the news of his illness. Joseph, normally so vigorous and energetic, just sat in a corner of the kitchen looking blankly out of the window, his black face puckered in sad bewilderment. It seemed impossible for Aunt Lou to stop crying, her noisy grief being in marked contrast to Mandy's white-faced, tearless restraint. She had been out when the cable arrived and it fell to Lin's lot to break to her the news of her father's illness.

'Darling, don't worry!' Lin put her arms round her. 'It probably isn't anything very serious.'

'He's got a bad heart.' Mandy's voice was a thin little thread. 'He said not to say anything to April, but he has.' Her face puckered suddenly. 'Where's Ruel? Has he gone to be with him? Couldn't he have taken me, too?'

'He wanted to get to your father as quickly as possible,' Lin reminded her gently.

'Will April go, too?'

'I expect so.' Lin glanced at her watch and came to a sudden decision. 'Look, Mandy, I've checked and there's a flight to Antigua in a couple of hours' time. I think I'm going to pack a suitcase for April so that when she comes in she can leave immediately if she wants to. Will you help me?'

Mandy nodded, pathetically anxious to be of use. They had half-packed one of April's expensive, monogrammed suitcases with bare essentials when the bedroom door suddenly burst open.

'What *are* you both doing?' April's face was a

mixture of astonishment and indignation as she took in the scene before her.

'April!' Lin went towards her with a cry of relief. 'I didn't hear you come in! April dear, it's Godfrey——'

'I know all about Godfrey!' April's voice was impatient. 'I've just had Aunt Lou weeping all over me! He was taken ill on the way home from New York, I gather? Well, Ruel's gone out to look after him so that'll be all right, thank goodness! I can't say I'm particularly keen on the idea of being stuck in a place like Antigua!' She looked at the litter of clothes on the bed and then turned to Lin with raised brows. 'You surely aren't packing that suit-case for me, are you?'

Lin said slowly, 'Do you mean—you don't want to go to Antigua?' She was painfully aware of Mandy standing still and silent beside her, her arms full of her stepmother's dainty lingerie.

'Oh, don't be silly, Lin!' April spoke irritably. 'What good will I be? You know I go absolutely to pieces when there's illness, I shouldn't be a scrap of use to poor Godfrey! Anyway, he's unconscious, isn't he—he won't know whether I'm there or not. Much better to leave things to Ruel. He can bring Godfrey home as soon as he's fit to travel: I'll make sure everything's ready for them here.'

Lin heard Mandy take a short breath and saw her take a step forward, her eyes burning in her small pale face. She spoke gently.

'Mandy, will you go downstairs and ask Aunt Lou to make us some coffee, please?'

Although she did not know it, her eyes pleaded

with the child not to make a scene. Mandy hesitated, then with one accusing look at her stepmother she went. April waited until the door closed behind her and then said peevishly, ' Really, Lin, you do seem to have taken rather a lot on yourself! You might have waited to ask me before you started manning panic stations!'

Lin said very clearly and distinctly, ' Have I got this right, April? Godfrey is ill, in hospital in Antigua, and you really don't want to join him?'

April's eyes fell under her cool gaze.

' There's no need to make me sound like a criminal! I—I hate illness, Lin! You know I do!' Her soft red lips quivered pathetically.

That at least was true. During her mother's illness April had visited her in hospital with obvious reluctance. It had been Lin who at the end had kept up an almost constant bedside vigil.

She said now, in a flat, tired voice, ' All right, April. It's up to you.'

She turned towards the bed and began emptying the suitcase with trembling hands. She felt curiously bereft. Ruel had gone, and she was beginning to think that April—the April she'd loved—had never existed, except perhaps in her imagination.

CHAPTER IX

For the next twenty-four hours Lin lived in a queer, exhausted, detached state. She read Ruel's letter over many times. Under normal circumstances her world would again have been drenched in sun and she would have become a dreamer of dreams, but these were not normal circumstances. Buonaventura was under a grim shadow which affected all its inhabitants. Aunt Lou and Joseph went about their duties wearing strained, anxious expressions and Mandy was a pale little ghost, refusing to stir from the house in case the telephone rang. Lin did her best to help and comfort her, but though the child clung closely to her there was really very little she could do to alleviate the burden of anxiety.

There had been one call from Ruel in Antigua. April had taken it in her bedroom and so Lin did not know what explanation, if any, she had offered for her decision to stay at Buonaventura. All she said, later, was that Godfrey's condition was unaltered and that he was still unconscious.

April was, in fact, the only one who was more or less her normal self. Lin, looking at her, wondered with an odd feeling of distaste just what her cousin's marriage vows had meant to her. She found herself hoping passionately that Godfrey would make a full and complete recovery, for it was obvious that April would have even less use for an ageing invalid husband than she had for an ageing vigorous one. Whatever hapened, she thought sadly, it was almost inevitable that one day Godfrey was destined to be sadly disillusioned, just as she herself had been. And Ruel. She no longer blamed Ruel for the bitter dislike he had never bothered to hide. Instead, she wondered at herself. How was it that she'd never before realized the full extent of April's selfishness, her callous disregard for anyone's wellbeing but her own? The answer, she finally decided, lay in the fact that while Aunt Bea was alive she had had a restraining influence on her daughter and she had never quite dared to let herself go. But now Aunt Bea was dead and money had brought with it not only arrogance but friends—like Luis Cortes—who openly encouraged her to flout the ordinary concepts of decency and good behaviour.

Would she care if Godfrey died? Lin very much doubted it. She would probably welcome the opportunity to be rich and free. As for Ruel and Mandy . . . but here Lin's thoughts came to a full stop. She could not bear to go any further.

Like everyone else April had not been out of the house since learning of Godfrey's illness. In fact she had spent most of the day in her room, leaving Lin and Aunt Lou to answer the telephone and to cope with the constant stream of sympathetic callers. ('I simply can't stand all the weeping and wailing!' she'd said irritably.) She joined Lin for dinner, however, and afterwards sat with her in the drawing room, listening to records. Or ostensibly listening to records. It was some time before Lin realized that she was unusually restless and on edge. She kept looking at the clock and several times she got up from her chair to wander aimlessly round the room, picking up a magazine and flicking desultorily through its pages, beating a tattoo with her fingernails on the windowsill, straightening a picture that was a little awry. It was not, Lin thought, that she seemed worried: frustrated would be the better word. But why?

On a small table in a corner of the room stood a crystal vase filled with some magnificent crimson flowers. They had been delivered to the house that morning and although there was no card with them Lin had guessed that they were probably from Luis. Now, as April bent over them, her expression abstracted, a suspicion that was almost a certainty leaped into her mind.

She said, careful to keep her voice light and casual, ' Isn't it tonight that Luis is holding a party aboard his yacht?'

April turned in a flash. ' Yes. Isn't it too sickening? I was looking forward to it so much: Luis throws simply marvellous parties!'

So she had guessed right! April was feeling resentful because with Godfrey critically ill even she dared not demonstrate her complete indifference by appearing at a party!

She said bitingly, ' Yes, too bad of Godfrey not to have arranged his heart attack for a more convenient time, wasn't it?'

April stared at her, flushing angrily, but before she could answer the telephone rang in the hall. She went swiftly to answer it, closing the door behind her, while Lin sat anxiously waiting, her hands clenched in her lap. Was it Ruel? With good—or bad—news?

One glance at April's face when she came back into the room after several minutes told her that whoever the caller had been it had not been Ruel. April was smiling, and it was what Ann had once called a 'cream-pot' smile.

' Just someone ringing up for the latest news of Godfrey,' she said airily. She sat down, yawning as she did so.

'Heavens, I'm tired. I didn't sleep a wink last night. I think I'll go to bed early tonight, Lin. You too, old thing, you look absolutely washed out.'

Lin looked at her, startled by the unexpected note of solicitude in her voice, but April's lovely face was perfectly innocent. She didn't look particularly tired and it was extremely unlikely that she really *had* spent a sleepless night, but on the other hand she certainly did seem to be yawning rather a lot. Lin found herself doing it, too, but then that was hardly surprising. She really had lain awake hour after hour, worrying and wondering about Godfrey, about April, about Ruel, about Mandy, about herself.

'Let's turn in now.' April's voice was persuasive. 'Honestly, Lin, I just can't keep my eyes open. A good night's sleep would do us both good.'

Startled but obedient, Lin agreed. Afterwards she was glad she had done so, for it was not until she was actually in bed that she realized that she was in fact tired to the point of utter exhaustion. She fell almost at once into a deep, dreamless sleep, and knew nothing else until she felt someone shaking her shoulder, rudely, almost violently.

Bewildered, still bemused with sleep, she opened her eyes. A white-clad figure was bending over her bed . . . *April!* April, in the beautiful white dress she had worn for her party, crying pitifully, her breath coming in gulping sobs.

'April! What is it?' Her heart thudding, Lin struggled into a sitting position and grabbed for the bedside switch. Half-past three! April had gone to bed hours ago! What on earth was she doing here, in a dance dress, at this hour?

April sank down on to the bed beside her. She took her hands away from her face and Lin almost gasped in horror. Her cheeks were ashen and her eyes were those of a hunted animal.

'Oh, Lin, I'm in trouble! Terrible, ghastly trouble!' Her shoulders shook with sobs. 'I'm frightened. Oh, Lin, help me!'

'*What is it?*' Lin was now as white as her cousin.

'Something dreadful's happened! Oh, I can't tell you! I'm ruined—ruined! Godfrey will never forgive me!'

Sick with apprehension, Lin put her arm round the heaving shoulders. 'April, don't cry so! Tell me! What's happened? Why are you dressed? You—you haven't been out?'

April's voice was muffled. 'Yes, I have. I—I went to the party—Luis' party.'

Lin was suddenly ice-cold. She waited. There was more to come.

April went on sobbing. After a moment or two, licking her lips, she said falteringly, 'I know I shouldn't have gone. I—I didn't mean to, honestly I didn't, Lin. But Luis rang up—you remember when I went to answer the phone? He—he sounded so disappointed when I said I couldn't come. He said—he said nobody would know if I just slipped out of the house when you were all asleep.'

Lin's face was rigid with shock. 'Then what happened?'

April pressed her hands to her head, shuddering violently. 'I thought everything was going to be all right. It was a marvellous party. Then there was an awful commotion.' She paused, licking her lips

146

again. 'It—it was the police. They boarded the yacht.'

'*The police?*'

'Yes. I—I don't know why. I didn't stop to find out.' April's voice shook. 'I got over the side. They—the police—saw me and somebody followed. I—I got into my car and drove away, as fast as I could.'

'And?' Lin whispered. So far she had heard only half the story, she was sure of that.

Was it her imagination, or did April hesitate? Then she drew a long shuddering breath. 'That's all. I—I got away. They didn't follow me here.'

Lin looked at her, at the white pinched face and tear-filled eyes. Gripping her by the shoulders, she said sharply, 'Then why are you so frightened? What did you mean—you were ruined?'

'I'm afraid they might have got the number of the car,' April said desperately. 'Lin, if they did they'll find out it was me! They'll know I was at that party! They might think I was taking drugs too—' She ended on a rising note of hysteria, clapping her hands to her mouth as if realizing that she had said too much.

'*Drugs?*'

April shivered. She said nothing, but looked away.

Lin felt sick to the pit of her stomach. She said slowly, 'Is *that* what Luis dabbles in—drugs? Is *that* how he made his money so quickly? And is *that* why the police raided his yacht?'

April gulped. She said wretchedly, 'I don't know. I—I didn't think it mattered. About the drugs, I mean.'

Lin felt as though she was in the grip of a hideous nightmare. She said despairingly, 'Oh, April, how *could* you?' and then could have kicked herself for the futility of the question.

April began to sob again and somehow Lin steadied herself. She said quietly, 'Have you any real reason to think the police got the number of your car?'

'They must have done!' April was wringing her hands now. 'Oh, Lin, what shall I do? There'll be such an awful scandal! It—it would have been bad enough at any time, but just now . . . with Godfrey so ill . . .' Her voice trailed away into nothing.

'But you haven't done anything *wrong*! I mean, not legally!' Lin was thinking hard. 'April, I don't see why the police should bother about you. And even if they do—well, all you've got to do is to make a statement and tell them the truth. You were at the party, but you weren't taking drugs! Surely that puts you in the clear?'

April gave a little moan. 'I know, I know! But it's bound to leak out that I was there, things like that always do!' She stopped, dabbing at her eyes with a wisp of a handkerchief. 'Lin, Godfrey will never forgive me if he finds out that I'm mixed up in a thing like this! You don't know him! He—he's so proud of his name, his honour! The scandal will kill him!'

She stopped, looking at her cousin imploringly. 'Oh, Lin, please help me!'

'But what can I do?' Lin asked helplessly. She

couldn't put the clock back, no matter how much she wanted to.

'You could pretend to be me,' April said on a sudden rush of breath.

Lin's heart suddenly began to beat faster. April's eyes were fixed on her, filled with a mixture of hope and dread.

She said harshly, 'What do you mean?'

April ran her tongue round her lips. 'Couldn't you say it was you at the party and not me? I—I could pretend that I knew all about it, that I lent you my car. The police wouldn't know any difference, they only caught a glimpse of me, and we're quite alike, from a distance. Nobody would give us away, Luis wouldn't let them.'

This wasn't happening. It couldn't be true. In a curiously flat, dead voice Lin said, 'No. No, we can't do that.'

'But *why*?' Suddenly April was clutching her arm with frantic fingers. 'Lin, why not? You're not like me! You've got nothing to lose!'

Nothing to lose! Lin was shaken by sudden anger. Nothing to lose—except Ruel! White-lipped, she said, 'It's impossible. I'm sorry, April, I can't do it.'

'I'll make it worth your while! Give you money . . . anything!' April began, then stopped, frightened into silence by the look Lin gave her. She began to shiver and cry in a hopeless sort of way.

'Lin, you just don't understand! That party, it—it wasn't like ordinary parties! People were . . . well, people were . . .'

'All right,' Lin said curtly. 'I can guess. So

149

what?'

'It'll be in the papers!' There was a note of pure hysteria in April's voice. 'All the details! Lin, it will ruin my marriage! Don't you care about that?'

Lin was silent and April drew a long breath. She said bitterly, 'I was sure *you* would help. You're the only one I can turn to. I—I haven't got anybody else.' She dropped her head on to her hands and added childishly, pathetically, 'Mummy said you'd promised that you'd always stand by me.'

'April, that's not fair!' Lin's voice rang out in protest.

April's lips quivered. 'No, it isn't. I'm sorry, Lin. I shouldn't have said that.' She paused, and for a moment her blue eyes were veiled by her thick lashes. Then she added, very softly, 'I wouldn't mind so much if other people weren't going to get hurt. Godfrey, Ruel, Mandy . . . the mud will stick to them.'

Lin got up and walked to the window. She felt curiously cold and empty. For a long time she stood staring out at the velvet sky with eyes that saw nothing. Then without turning round she said drearily, 'All right, April, you win. If I'm asked I'll say it was me.'

'Lin!' April's voice was a gasp of gratitude. 'Oh, Lin, I knew you wouldn't let me down! I'll make it up to you! I'll—'

Gently Lin disengaged herself from her cousin's fervent embrace and checked the eager protestations. 'Go and get some sleep, April.'

'Sleep in spite of thunder ' . . . Lin's lips quivered as April—a much calmer, happier April—went back to her own room. There wouldn't be any more sleep for her tonight. She was under no illusions as to what she had done. April's marriage might be saved, but it was very possibly only at the expense of her own happiness. 'I trust you, Lin' . . . Ruel's words came back to her with bitter poignancy. Would he trust her after this?

She would have liked to cry—it would have relieved some of the unbearable ache inside her—but her unhappiness was too great to find an outlet in tears. She thought of what Ann would have said—almost certainly that April wasn't worth it. Well, she wasn't. But there wasn't only April to be considered. As she herself had pointed out, the whole family was involved. They would all have to suffer her disgrace.

She crouched by the window until dawn streaked the sky. Then she got up. This was a new day and she had to be ready to face whatever might come.

It came earlier than she had expected, in the shape of a car containing two men, one young, one approaching middle-age. They were wearing a uniform with which she had become familiar—grey shorts and shirts, blue and white armbands and black, flat-peaked caps—but even without it she would have known who they were. The police. For a moment she stood watching them from her window, her face going very white, then she turned and ran to wake April.

It wasn't necessary. April was already awake and judging from the overflowing ash tray beside her had been chain-smoking for hours. She was still very pale and heavy eyed, but seemed to have recovered something of her usual poise.

' April! The police are here! '

April stubbed out her cigarette. ' Already? They don't let the grass grow under their feet, do they? ' She gave a quick glance into the mirror. Subconsciously Lin noted that she was not wearing make-up: she looked just as beautiful without it, but oddly young and defenceless.

She caught hold of Lin's arm as they were going downstairs. ' Lin, you—you won't forget that you're going to say it was you? '

' No,' Lin said quietly. ' No, I won't forget,' and wondered whether the waiting police would be able to hear the thumping of her heart.

Aunt Lou had shown them into the little sitting room and they were standing by the window when April and Lin went in. The elder was a kind-looking man with eyes that had laughter crinkles at the corners: the younger was a solemn-looking youth armed with a notebook and a variety of pencils.

April went swiftly forward, holding out her hand. ' Good morning! '

' Good morning, ma'am.' The elder man—an Inspector—did not return her smile, though there was a distinct gleam of admiration in his colleague's rather protuberant eyes. April was apt to have a somewhat devastating effect on susceptible males, Lin thought wryly, and even policemen were only human.

The Inspector, dispensing with the usual preliminaries, was speaking in a cool, measured voice.

' Mrs Selby, will you please tell me if you left this house last night to attend a party given by Mr Luis

Cortes aboard his yacht, *Starlight?*'

April's blue eyes opened wide. Lin, watching her, found herself thinking that she hadn't wasted her time at drama school after all.

' Why, no, Inspector. I—I was very tired and—and also worried about my husband, who is ill in Antigua. I went to bed rather earlier than usual. It was my cousin—' She hesitated and glanced at Lin, standing silently in the background.

Lin drew a deep breath and stepped forward. She said steadily, ' Can I help you, Inspector? I was a guest at Mr Cortes' party.'

There was a moment's silence as for the first time the Inspector looked straight at her. Then he cleared his throat.

' You are—?'

' My name is Linda Grierson. I—I'm a visitor to Tobago.' She wondered if she looked as guilty as she felt. She had always been the world's worst liar.

' I see.' The Inspector's voice was expressionless. He added, ' It might have been wiser if you had allowed us to make your aquaintance last night, Miss Grierson.'

' I—I'm sorry.' Even to her own ears Lin's voice sounded flat and unreal, like that of a third-rate actress in a fourth-rate play. ' I—I know I shouldn't have run away. I was—frightened.' She stopped. Dear heaven, she thought, don't let him start asking me questions about the party . . .

But the Inspector didn't seem interested in the party. ' What happened after you left the yacht, Miss Grierson?'

Lin stared. The question was so unexpected.

'Why, I went home, of course.'

'And did you have an uneventful journey?' The Inspector's voice was very soft, his face bland, but Lin suddenly began to feel afraid.

'I—yes, quite uneventful.'

April came forward swiftly, flinging her arm round Lin's shoulders. Her indignation was beautifully done. Lin, remembering the hysteria of only a few short hours ago, could only marvel.

'Inspector, what *is* all this? What are all these questions leading up to? What do you think my cousin has done? You surely don't intend to arrest her merely because she was a guest at what was apparently rather a disreputable party?'

The Inspector's eyes were very cold. He said bleakly, 'Mrs Selby, it is only fair to warn you that your cousin will be extremely fortunate if she doesn't find herself facing a charge of manslaughter.'

'Manslaughter!' The word was wrenched from Lin's lips. Wild-eyed, she stared at the Inspector.

He took a step towards her, and for the first time his mask slipped. His voice was suddenly vibrant with anger.

'The man you hit last night—hit and left by the roadside—is seriously ill in hospital. If he dies—' He stopped.

Lin put her hand to her head. This was nonsense. It wasn't happening. She said dizzily, 'I—I don't understand. *What* man? I didn't hit anybody!' She looked beyond the Inspector at April, and saw with a pang of indescribable terror that her face had gone suddenly ashen.

'Come, Miss Grierson! Are you going to deny

that you were involved in an accident last night?' There was hostility now in the Inspector's eyes, and his face was very hard. 'It won't do you any good, you know. We've already checked the damage done to Mrs Selby's car.'

April said, in a queer choked voice, 'This—this is awful. Inspector, I don't know what to say!'

'I'm sorry, Mrs Selby. This must be a great shock to you, especially on top of your husband's illness.' The Inspector's voice had softened into wonderful kindness. 'But facts are facts. Your cousin knocked a man down last night and didn't have the humanity to stop and see what she'd done.' He paused, then added grimly, 'Hit-and-run drivers don't merit much sympathy from anyone, Mrs Selby.'

Lin said nothing. If her life had depended on it she would have been unable to speak. If what had happened last night had been a nightmare, this was even worse. Her hands were clenched into icy knots, her whole brain seemed numb.

The sergeant said, 'Do you want to make a statement now, Miss Grierson? and she shook her head. She said, 'I didn't do it. I didn't knock anybody down,' but though the sergeant wrote her words down she knew he didn't believe her.

April was speaking to the Inspector. Lin caught the words 'Later' and 'When the shock's worn off I'll bring her down to the station' and then as suddenly as they had come the policemen had gone, and she and April were left facing each other, one on each side of an otherwise empty room.

There was a long silence. Then Lin said, 'Why

didn't you tell me about the man? Why, April, why?' Even as she asked the question she knew the answer. April had known only too well what her reaction would have been.

April said in a whisper, 'I—I didn't know he was badly hurt. I swear to you I didn't know, Lin. I thought he might have been all right.' She stopped, biting her lip. 'He—he may not die, even now. The Inspector said—'

'I don't care what the Inspector said!' Suddenly Lin recovered the full use of her numbed faculties. Her eyes blazing in her white face, she stared at her cousin. 'April, do you really think I'm going to take the blame for your carelessness— your cowardice? Face a possible charge of manslaughter?' She stopped, struggling for control. 'Do you really think I'm going to let you get away with that?'

There was another silence. Then April said softly, 'You really haven't got much choice, have you, Lin?' There was a curious note in her voice—a note which somehow struck a chill into Lin's heart.

She said, 'You've admitted to being at the party, Lin. Don't you think the Inspector would find it rather—odd—if you were to go to him now with the truth? What do you think he'd say if you suddenly upped and told him it was me all the time?'

Lin stared at her. 'What do you mean? When you own up—' Then she saw. Her voice dwindled and stopped. She said incredulously, 'You mean— you're really going to let *me* take the blame for what *you* did?'

April said nothing, but the hard glitter in her blue

eyes spoke for her. Lin stood staring at her for a few seconds longer and then with a little gasp she ran out of the room and into the cloakroom, where she was suddenly, violently sick.

CHAPTER X

When she emerged, still in a state of shock, moving almost like a sleepwalker, the telephone started to ring just as she passed it. Almost automatically she lifted the receiver, just as she had done so many times during the past twenty-four hours, and it was with a queer sense of unreality that she heard a voice at the other end of the line say, 'A call for you from Antigua.'

'Lin?' It was Ruel who spoke next, and at the sound of his deep, pleasant tones Lin's heart jumped into her throat. Here was a blessed link with sanity! She stood clutching the receiver in a suddenly damp hand, almost overcome by the longing which swept over her. She tried to say something, but her throat was parched and her lips shaking so that no words would come.

'Lin? Are you still there?' Ruel's voice was suddenly peremptory.

'I . . . yes.' With a tremendous effort Lin pulled herself together. This wasn't the time to be emotive. 'Do you want to speak to April?'

There was a pause at the other end of the line. Then Ruel said curtly, 'No, I think you'd better break it to her. Lin, Godfrey died an hour ago. He never recovered consciousness.'

'Ruel! Oh, Ruel, I'm so sorry!' Instantly Lin forgot her own troubles in a rush of swift compassion. She knew that Godfrey had meant a great deal to Ruel: although not his real father, he had yet been the only father he had ever known. And Mandy . . . what about poor little Mandy?

As if he read her thoughts Ruel said, almost hesitatingly, 'I have no right to ask this, Lin, but would *you* please tell Mandy? I needn't tell you that she's going to be very upset. If you could break it to her gently . . .'

Lin said quickly, 'Yes, of course I'll tell her if you want me to.' April wouldn't mind . . . it was awful to have to break that kind of news to a child, she'd probably have shirked the job in any case.

Ruel said, 'You'd better tell April that there wouldn't be any point in her coming here now. The funeral will be over before she could possibly get here. In the tropics . . .' He did not go on.

'I know. I understand.' Lin could not bear the pain in his voice, even though he was doing his best to hide it.

'Dear Lin!' Once those words would have lifted her to heaven, but now they hurt almost unbearably. Ruel must have heard her sudden quick intake of breath, for he spoke sharply.

'Lin! Is anything the matter?' Then, as she did not immediately answer, 'Are you all right?'

April had appeared behind her. Lin said quickly, 'Yes, I'm all right. Here's April. Goodbye, Ruel,' and put the receiver down before turning to face her cousin.

There was hostility and suspicion in April's face.

' Who's that? Who were you speaking to?'

' She's afraid I was telephoning the police,' Lin thought wonderingly. Aloud she said quietly, ' It was Ruel, April. It—it's bad news, I'm afraid.'

For a moment April stood very still. Then, perfectly composed, she said coolly, ' Godfrey's dead?'

' Yes. I'm—I'm terribly sorry, April.'

April said nothing for a minute or two. At last she said, with a detachment that struck Lin as being almost heartless, ' Am I expected to go to the funeral?'

' Ruel said it would all be over before you could possibly get there.' Lin hesitated. ' April, would you mind if I told Mandy?'

There was a flicker of relief in April's blue eyes. ' Heavens, no! I'd be very grateful. I simply couldn't face it! Perhaps you'd tell Aunt Lou and Joseph too, while you're about it.' She paused, then added almost pleadingly, ' Look, Lin, about that other business——'

Couldn't she even spare a few minutes to mourn the husband who had loved her? Lin said unsteadily, ' I'm sorry, April. I don't want to discuss that now. Let me know if there's anything else you want me to do.'

She turned and fled up the stairs. How much difference would it have made if Godfrey had died yesterday instead of today? Would April still have gone to that ill-starred party? And would she, Lin, have agreed to help her, knowing that there was now no question of her marriage being in jeopardy? If . . . what was it Ruel had said? ' What's the good of " ifs "?' Lin gave a little sob. The future stretched out in front of her, black and menacing, but she dared not think about it now. Mandy came first.

The schoolroom, where Mandy had lessons with Miss Purley, was at the end of a long corridor. Lin was halfway along it when Aunt Lou suddenly emerged from the stillroom where she had been carefully putting away piles of snowy laundry.

In her haste Lin would have passed her by without a word, but Aunt Lou put a gnarled and trembling hand on her arm.

' Missy Lin, is there—is there any more news?'

Looking into those anxious, pleading eyes, Lin found it impossible to lie or prevaricate. Gently she drew Aunt Lou into the stillroom, closing the door behind them, and told her that Godfrey was dead. As she had feared, the faithful old servant took it very badly, burying her face in her ample apron, her massive shoulders heaving with silent sobs, and it was some time before Lin felt able to leave her. At least, she thought, even if April was dry-eyed Godfrey had somebody to weep for him . . .

Just as she reached the schoolroom the door opened and Miss Purley came out.

' Oh, good morning, Miss Grierson! Have you by any chance seen Mandy?'

Lin was startled by the elder woman's somewhat annoyed expression.

' Why no, Miss Purley. Actually I was just coming to find her.' She glanced at her watch. ' I thought she normally had lessons with you at this time?'

'Well, yes, but I sent her down to Mrs Selby about ten minutes ago. She's got toothache rather badly, she's been almost crying with pain this morning. In the end I told her she simply couldn't go on like this and that she'd have to ask Mrs Selby to make an appointment for her to see the dentist. I thought she'd only be gone a minute.'

Lin was staring at her in dismay. There was one possible explanation for Mandy's prolonged absence —but surely, after what April had said, she would never have told the child about her father?

She said breathlessly, ' Mandy's in trouble, Miss Purley. Her father has died: the news came a short time ago.' Ignoring the governess's shocked exclamation, she turned quickly. She must find April and Mandy at once!

Halfway down the stairs she met April—alone.

' April! Where's Mandy?' She stopped, realizing with sudden incredulous dismay that her cousin's face was flushed and angry. What on earth had happened to upset her?

' How should I know?' April snapped the words out. ' She went flying out of the house like a bat out of hell! I couldn't have stopped her if I'd tried!'

Lin looked at her. ' Oh, April! You didn't tell her about Godfrey?'

' I had to tell her. She knew from my face something was wrong,' April said sullenly, and Lin thought: ' You're lying . . .'

Unable to keep the anxiety out of her voice, she said, ' You did break it to her gently? What did she say?'

April made an impatient gesture. ' Oh, for

heaven's sake, Lin, don't fuss! She had to know some time! As for breaking it to her gently . . . her father's dead and that's that, however much you wrap it up in high-falutin' words!'

Lin's face was very white. She said unsteadily, 'You should have left it to me! You said you would!'

April's eyes glittered. It came to Lin suddenly that she was in a vile temper. 'Who's her stepmother—you or me?'

'Excuse me!' Miss Purley spoke quietly behind them. 'I've just been speaking to Joseph. He is working in the garden and he says Mandy rushed past him down the drive a few minutes ago. Evidently she has decided to play truant for to-day.'

'Well, you'd better see to it that she's punished when she returns!' April snapped. 'And now, if you'll excuse me, I want to get ready to go out!'

Lin looked at the governess. 'She knows about her father. I must go and find her.'

Miss Purley shook her head. 'I'm afraid the damage has already been done. Let her get the worst of her grief over in private, Miss Grierson. She'll come back when she has no more tears to shed.'

Lin's face set in anxious lines. Miss Purley was probably right, but a situation like this must have been precisely what Ruel had feared and tried to avoid. She felt that she had let him down badly, although under the circumstances it was hardly her fault.

Her anxiety increased as the day wore on and there was still no sign of Mandy. If only she knew what really had happened between April and her stepdaughter! Mandy had obviously said something which had put April in a towering rage—but what? And how had April retaliated? She had questioned Joseph closely and what he had told her had caused her grave misgivings. The child had apparently been almost beside herself when she had rushed out of the house: she hadn't even thought of taking Argos with her. Where could she have gone? And what was she doing? She tried to tell herself that it was most unlikely that she would come to any harm: she knew practically the whole of the island like the back of her hand. Nevertheless, the thought of her lonely and comfortless, probably sobbing her heart out in some lonely retreat, was intolerable. Whatever else she forgave April for, she would never forgive her for this.

She spent the whole afternoon searching for Mandy in the immediate vicinity of Buonaventura, but met with no success. By nightfall she was really worried and she knew that even Aunt Lou and Joseph, who were accustomed to Mandy's wanderings, were beginning to share her own misgivings.

April did not return until eight o'clock. Lin did not know where she had been, nor did she particularly care, but in her desperation she met her at the door.

'April, Mandy is still missing!'

'Oh, she'll turn up sooner or later,' April said, as calmly as if she were talking about an item of lost property. She was, Lin noticed, wearing black . . . in which she always looked stunning. She knew that, of course. Wearing widow's weeds wouldn't be any hardship for April . . . for a few days, at least.

'I think we ought to ring the police,' Lin persisted stubbornly.

April looked up at her and laughed. 'My *dear* Lin! Haven't you had enough of policemen for one day?' She flicked the ash from the end of her cigarette. 'Which reminds, me, did I tell you that Inspector Bailey wants to see you at the police station tomorrow afternoon? I'm afraid he'll want a statement from you about last night. You *are* going to be sensible, aren't you, darling? Because I'm afraid that Luis is quite prepared to swear on oath that it was you he entertained last night and that he never as much as clapped eyes on me.'

Lin put her hand to her head. Somehow or another she had managed to push that whole ghastly business to the back of her mind. Her fear and anxiety for Mandy had absorbed her thoughts to the exclusion of everything else.

She said chokily, 'April, it's *Mandy* I'm worried about, not you or me!'

'Then you're making a very great mistake.' April's eyes had narrowed suddenly. She added sweetly, 'Don't you even want to know about the man Inspector Bailey thinks you knocked down? I rang the hospital on your behalf, wasn't it nice of me? You'll be glad to know he isn't dead—yet.'

Lin looked at her. Then she said, very levelly, 'April, are you going to ring the police and tell them about Mandy, or shall I?'

There was a moment's silence, then April gave the faintest of shrugs and moved towards the telephone.

It was the longest night Lin had ever known.

Even April, when ten o'clock came and there was still no sign of Mandy, became uneasy, although her manner was tinged a little with defiance. Perhaps, Lin thought, her conscience was pricking her . . . if she still had a conscience. Even so, she was the only one who went to bed. Lin and Aunt Lou sat up all night, drinking vast quantities of black coffee, each wrapped up in her own thoughts. Lin's were of Ruel as well as of Mandy. Oh, if only Mandy could be found before he returned home from Antigua! If on top of his grief at Godfrey's death he had to bear this crushing anxiety as well . . . She shivered. There was this other ghastly, night-marish business too. April was evidently quite determined that she was not going to be implicated in any way whatever, and who would believe her, Lin? April was the wife . . . widow, rather . . . of a wealthy and respected plantation owner, the police would obviously accept her word rather than that of a penniless nobody from England.

' I've only myself to blame,' she thought. ' I should never have agreed to lie in the first place.' She wondered what Ruel would say when he found out, and sighed sharply. It wasn't difficult to imagine his reaction. She would tell him the truth, since it could no longer hurt Godfrey, but it was unlikely to make much difference. A story like that would stretch anyone's credulity, and Ruel was such a stranger to trust, anyway.

By daybreak the inaction, and the vivid pictures conjured up by her over-active imagination, were beginning to tell on her nerves. She got to her feet with sudden resolution. Anything was better than just sitting here, waiting.

She spoke gently to Aunt Lou. 'I'm going to borrow April's car and drive down to Mareo Bay. There are such a lot of trees and rocks there . . . it's just possible that Mandy is hiding. Or—or she might have fallen and hurt herself.'

The old woman nodded dully. Grief and anxiety had told on her, too: she looked shrivelled and diminished.

Lin did not bother to wake April to ask if she could borrow the car. She wouldn't be gone long, anyway. It was a heavenly day, but for once she did not rejoice in the sunshine, and the perfection of Mareo Bay, when she reached it, left her unmoved. For a long time she searched patiently among the rocks and trees, calling Mandy's name, but without success. Then she looked out to sea, and her heart gave a jump. Caught on a jutting-out rock, some few hundred yards from the shore, was something blue and white. Blue and white . . . that was the colour of the dress Mandy had been wearing yesterday! Could the child possibly have come here to swim? If something had happened . . . if her discarded clothes had then somehow been carried away on the tide . . . Lin shivered as a terrible fear began to take shape in her mind.

There was only one way to find out. Racing down to the water's edge, she stripped off her pink candy-stripe cotton dress and in briefs and bra plunged into the water. She kept her eyes fixed on the rock and forged steadily towards it, swimming strongly. Inevitably the rock was further away than she had thought, and long before she reached it she began to tire, but she still kept going. At last her fingers touched the smooth slippery surface of the rock and panting and breathless, brushing her streaming hair off her face, she clambered on to it. Fearfully she bent to examine the blue and white material, and a second later expelled her breath in a huge sigh of relief. Not Mandy's dress but a towel . . . somebody else had been swimming here and been careless!

Almost laughing in her relief, she slid back into the water, and it was not until she had swum several strokes that she realized that she might have been sensible to have rested longer. She had swum a long way and she was tired. For a moment she debated the wisdom of returning to the rock, then she decided to keep going. At best the rock was an uncomfortable perch!

She was more than halfway when she first noticed the figure on the beach. Almost at the same moment she was aware of a nasty undertow and for the first time became slightly panicky. For some time now her strokes had become slower and slower: she was so tired that she simply hadn't the strength to fight a sea that wasn't going her way. Her arms felt like cottonwool, her legs like lead, and the shore seemed a long, long way away. Suddenly she knew she wasn't going to make it, and the man on the shore seemed to know it, too, for even as she battled against the remorseless waves she saw him stripping off his clothes in what appeared to be frantic haste.

Desperately she tried to flog her tired body into making one last effort. If only she could keep going until help reached her! She stopped, treading water, trying to stifle the panic which welled up inside her.

Then a huge wave hit her, and another, and suddenly she was gasping and floundering, her lungs were full of sea-water and there was a dreadful roaring in her ears.

'*I'm drowning!*' Even as the thought came into her head she felt strong hands grip her shoulders and she knew no more until she found herself lying, gasping and shivering, on the warm sand. Vaguely she became aware that someone was speaking to her, that someone's hands were rubbing her into warmth. Somebody tall and dark-haired, with a brown face . . . somebody who knew her name.

She opened her eyes and said uncertainly, disbelievingly, 'Ruel . . . ?'

He said, almost fiercely, 'Don't try to talk. You're all right, darling, you're safe.'

Of course it was a dream . . . Ruel was still in Antigua. From sheer force of habit she put out her hand and pinched herself, and at her surprised 'Ouch!' Ruel burst out laughing. Suddenly he bent over her and picked her up, cradling her in his arms, his cheek against her wet hair.

'I'm real enough, darling. You're not dreaming this time either.' He bent his head and kissed her lips. Then he said huskily, 'Lucky for you that I am real! You nearly drowned! Lin, why did you do it?'

Of course he didn't know about Mandy! Lin twisted in his arms, her eyes wide and dark in her pale face.

'Ruel! Mandy——'

'Is quite safe. Right this minute she's home, in bed, and fast asleep,' Ruel told her, and Lin gasped.

'But she can't be! Ruel, she—she ran away yesterday. I came here this morning to look for her——'

'I know. Aunt Lou told me where you'd gone.' Ruel's voice was very gentle. 'Darling, the police found Mandy early this morning, hiding in a cave on the hillside. They took her home ten minutes after you'd left.'

'Oh, Ruel!' Tears of relief and reaction welled up in Lin's eyes and trickled down her cheeks. 'Thank God they found her!' Then, sharply, 'Is she all right?'

'Very hungry, very tired, rather frightened. The doctor's been to see her: he gave her a sedative and thinks she'll be as right as rain when she wakes up.'

'Have you seen her?'

'I arrived home shortly after she'd been put to bed. I peeped into her room, but she was already fast asleep.' His arm tightened round Lin's shoulders. 'I wanted you and you weren't there. Thank goodness you had the sense to tell Aunt Lou where you were going!'

Lin shut her eyes. She felt Ruel wiping the tears from her cheeks and she said unsteadily, 'Ruel, please don't be so kind. I—I've got something to tell you. Something you'll have to know.'

There was a moment's silence. Then very deliberately he said, 'You don't have to tell me anything, Lin. I already know.'

Lin's eyes flew open, searching his face. 'I don't understand. What do you know?'

'That you're a silly, misguided little idiot with the most ridiculous ideas about loyalty I've ever

169

known!' he told her forcefully. He felt her shiver and gave her a swift hard hug.

'I think we'd better continue this conversation in the car. Here, put this on,' and he tossed her the cotton frock she'd discarded. 'You'll be all right —the rest of your clothes have dried on you, haven't they?'

Suddenly aware that the wisps of nylon which served as her undergarments hardly ranked as conventional beach wear, Lin hastily donned her dress. When she had finished Ruel swung her up into his arms and carried her to the car. She protested, but without a great deal of conviction, for she still felt extremely weak and shaky.

Ruel put her into the passenger seat, but though he slid behind the wheel he made no effort to start the car. Nor did he put his arm round her again. Instead he said quietly, 'Inspector Bailey was at the house when I arrived, Lin. It was he who found Mandy.'

She said nothing and after a moment he went on, 'He seemed very interested in your whereabouts. When I enquired why he told me what sort of a mess you were in.'

Lin said breathlessly, 'Ruel . . .' and put her hands up to her face.

Ruel said very deliberately, 'I told Bailey not to be a bloody fool. I told him that you weren't capable of running over a rabbit, let alone a human being, and that if he really believed you were a hit-and-run driver he needed his head examining. I also told him that if he tried to pin anything on you he'd have me to reckon with, and that I'd prove your innocence if I had to spend every cent I'd got.'

'You mean . . . you didn't believe it?'

She heard him take a quick breath. Then he said quietly, 'Darling, I may be all sorts of a fool, but even I'm not enough of a fool to believe you did what Bailey thinks you did. I meant what I said in that letter, Lin. I do trust you.' He paused. 'It was April, of course?'

It was really more of a statement than a question. Almost inaudibly Lin said, 'Yes. Ruel, I told the Inspector that I was at that party. I've got no proof that I wasn't and—and April won't own up.'

Ruel pulled her to him. 'Won't she? We'll see about that.'

Lin surrendered to his long, close embrace. Later —a long time later—she said huskily, 'I can't quite believe it yet. You wouldn't listen to me that day I came to the cottage. I was sure you'd hate me for ever when you found out what I was supposed to have done.'

He said wryly, 'You were right about my having lived with hate and suspicion for so long that I'd forgotten how to trust people. I think I loved you from the very first, Lin, right from the moment I saw you looking like a little girl who had strayed into wonderland, but I didn't dare to acknowledge it, even to myself. I couldn't afford to be hurt a second time.' He paused. 'I think I'd better tell you about that first time. You've probably already heard a very distorted version from April.'

'Ruel, you don't have to tell me——'

'I want you to understand, Lin. I was very much in love with Francine. Calf love, perhaps, but nevertheless to me it was very deep, very real. We were engaged. I thought she was the most wonderful girl in the world and I trusted her absolutely.' His mouth twisted. 'Then she—changed. I couldn't understand why, until I discovered quite by chance that she was having an affair with Luis. When I challenged her at first she denied it, then she flung my ring in my face and said that she no longer loved me . . . that she was going to marry Cortes. Four months later she drowned herself. She was pregnant . . . hooked on drugs which Cortes had supplied her with . . . and completely beside herself because he had refused to marry her.'

'Ruel, how dreadful!' Lin's voice was a shaken whisper.

'Yes. I nearly killed Cortes. I would have killed him, I think, if Godfrey hadn't intervened, just in time. Cortes left the island and so did I. The only difference was that I left to find forgetfulness and he left to make money out of vice.'

'You know he still traffics in drugs?'

'I guessed as much, and of course Bailey confirmed it. Unfortunately there won't be any charges arising out of that goddam party, but unofficially Cortes has been given the order of the boot. If he sticks around here much longer he'll find himself in trouble up to his worthless neck.'

He sighed sharply. 'I tried to warn April about him, but she wouldn't have it. Not that I'm really surprised. They're two of a kind, I'm afraid.' He stopped, his expression brooding. 'In a way things may have happened for the best—for Godfrey, I mean. Sooner or later April would have broken his heart or ruined him—or both.'

Her saw her lips quiver and kissed her again.

' You poor kid, you look whacked. I'm going to get you back to the house as soon as I can and put you to bed like Mandy. How much sleep did you have last night? None? Then don't argue, my girl! To bed you'll go, and I shall stand guard outside your room to make sure that no one disturbs you till I give the word!'

CHAPTER XI

He was as good as his word. It was dark when Lin awoke from a deep refreshing slumber to find Aunt Lou standing by her bedside with a cup of coffee.

' Feeling better, Missy Lin?' Aunt Lou was beaming again.

' Oh, miles better, thank you, Aunt Lou! Heavens, is that really the time? I've been asleep for *hours!*' Aghast, she began to dress at express speed. It was not only sleep that had refreshed her, the knowledge that Ruel loved and believed in her had given her new hope and confidence. Whatever the future held for her, she could meet it with courage as long as she had Ruel beside her.

He was waiting for her outside Mandy's room and they went in together. Mandy, like Lin, had just woken up. Her eyes were still wide and dark with grief for her father but no longer with despair.

She said in a small voice, ' I'm sorry I ran away, Lin. Were you very worried?'

' I was, rather.' Lin knelt and kissed her. ' But it's all right now. You're home again.'

' And Ruel.' Mandy looked up at her tall brother somewhat apprehensively. ' Are you cross with me, Ruel?'

' Of course I'm not.' Ruel took the small hand in his big brown one. ' Tell me one thing, though. What made you run away?'

Mandy shivered. ' It was April . . . she was so angry!'

' Angry?' Ruel and Lin spoke together.

' Miss Purley made me go down to see her because I'd got toothache so badly. She was talking to someone on the telephone. She was laughing a lot and calling the person " darling " and—and I thought of Daddy and I couldn't bear it. I said things to her and then she told me Daddy was dead and that she was in charge of me now and that if I wasn't good she'd send me away to England to the horridest school she could find.' She gulped. ' I said you wouldn't let her, Ruel, and she said you didn't matter any more and I'd never see you again.'

Ruel's face was black with anger. ' The little—'

Mandy's lips quivered. ' It isn't true, is it? She can't send me away?'

' Over my dead body!' Ruel said grimly.

Lin said gently, to divert the child's thoughts, ' What about your toothache, Mandy? Is it better?'

' A bit.' Mandy looked at her. ' It was dreadfully bad the night before last. I went to your room twice to ask you if I could have some of your aspirins, but you were so sound asleep you didn't hear me, and I didn't like to wake you.'

' Oh, but I wouldn't have minded—' Lin began, when Ruel interrupted her.

He said in a strange voice, ' You went to Lin's room the night before last? Mandy, *what time was it?*'

Mandy stared at him. ' About midnight, the first time. Then quite a long time after that.'

Ruel relaxed with a long sigh. Then he looked at Lin, smiling triumphantly as comprehension dawned in her eyes.

' Proof, Lin? I think even Inspector Bailey will be satisfied with that!' He rose to his feet, holding out his hand. ' Come, darling. It's time you had things out with your precious cousin!'

Mandy looked from one to the other, her eyes widening. ' You're holding hands and you called her darling! Ruel, are you going to marry Lin?'

Ruel laughed. ' I am. Any objections, young lady?'

' No. I think it's super,' Mandy said simply, and hugged them both.

' I'm afraid April won't agree with her.' Outside the bedroom Lin turned ruefully to Ruel. ' She'll be furious, I'm afraid.'

' She knows already. I told her,' Ruel said. There was a gleam of humour in his grey eyes as he added, ' As for her being furious—that, my darling, is the understatement of the year.' He laughed. ' What annoys her most, I think, is that you've succeeded where she has failed! April rather hoped, at one time, that I would be another conquest!'

Lin shivered. She could well believe that April's chief emotion was chagrin, but even she was unprepared for the torrent of abuse her cousin hurled at her before Ruel intervened. Without raising his voice he told her exactly what he thought of her and exactly what was in store for her when Inspector Bailey was told the truth about the identity of the hit-and-run driver.

'You've sheltered behind Lin for the last time,' he told her grimly. 'From now on you fight your own battles without her to help you. Incidentally, I shall see to it that Mandy isn't left in your tender care. Her home will be with Lin and me.'

'And where do you think that will be?' April's voice was sibilant with hate. 'Buonaventura is mine now, Ruel, and by God I'll see to it that you never set foot on my land again as long as you live! You can clear out today, all three of you! I won't have you in my house a moment longer!'

Ruel scratched his chin. Then very quietly he said, 'Don't you think you'd better study Godfrey's will before you start issuing ultimatums, April?'

She stared at him. 'I don't need to look at any will! Godfrey told me that he'd leave me everything he owned!' Her eyes glittered with malice. 'You didn't know that, did you?'

'Oh, but I did!' Ruel drawled. 'You've just made one little mistake, Mrs Selby. Buonaventura belongs to me. It wasn't Godfrey's in the first place, so there was never any question of his leaving it to you.'

'I don't believe you!' April's voice was suddenly shrill and breathless.

Ruel shrugged. 'It doesn't matter whether you

176

believe me or not. The lawyers will confirm what I say. Buonaventura belonged to my father. When he died he left it to my mother and when *she* died she left it to Godfrey, in trust, for his lifetime.'

Lin was looking at him wide-eyed, remembering the night she had told him that April thought he was jealous because he had been deprived of his ' rights '. What was it he'd said? ' How very amusing ... .' No wonder, she thought dazedly, that he'd laughed!

April's face was a sickly green. ' You mean—I get nothing?'

' I wouldn't say that. But of course you'd have had a lot more if you hadn't spent your married life trying to see how quickly you could spend how much.' Ruel's voice was grim. ' Godfrey lost that lawsuit, you know, April. That was what caused his heart attack. Even if he'd lived the spending jamboree would have been over.'

April stared at him, her face working. Then she rushed past him and a few moments later they heard the slam of the front door, followed by the sound of a car engine being started.

Lin was very pale. She said miserably ' Oh, Ruel, I wish it didn't have to be this way! I—I thought I hated her, but I don't. Even now, after all that she's done, I can't hate her.'

Ruel came over to her and put his arms round her, holding her close. ' You can't hate her because you're you, Lin. But she's brought her punishment on herself, darling. People like April can't expect to escape scot free for ever.'

Lin's face was set in anxious lines. ' Where will she go? What will she do?'

Ruel shrugged. 'I don't know and I can't say I honestly care. I shouldn't wonder if she didn't throw her lot in with Cortes.' He shook her gently by the shoulders. 'Stop worrying about her, darling. It's over and done with. It's the future that matters now—our future.' He twined a strand of her long, silky hair around his finger. 'Will you mind starting married life with a ready-made family?' The grey eyes laughed down into hers.

Lin forced an answering smile, though her heart was still heavy. 'If you mean Mandy, I can't think of anything nicer.'

'I can!' Ruel told her, and promptly proved it. Later, when she could speak, she asked hesitantly, 'Will we live here, at Buonaventura?'

He looked down at her. 'Not if you don't want to. I love the old place, but I'd be happy anywhere with you.' He paused, then added, 'Anyway, I shall sell the plantation. I'm not cut out to be a plantation owner: I never have been. What I'd really like to do—with your permission, darling!— is to go on painting. I've been promised an exhibition in New York soon.'

'Oh, Ruel, that's marvellous!' Lin's face lit up. 'You've got too great a gift to let it go to waste!'

'There's probably more money in coconuts than in landscapes!' Ruel warned her, but Lin only laughed and shook her head.

'I don't care if you don't make any money at all!'

'I said you were living in wonderland!' Ruel mocked her. He rumpled her hair. 'Where would you like to spend your honeymoon? New York? Paris? Vienna?'

Lin gave him a shy smile and shook her head again. 'None of those places.'

'Not *London?*' he asked in mock horror.

'Certainly not! Your island, Ruel! I'm longing to see it. Could we go there?'

She heard him catch his breath. 'My island? Darling, are you sure? No people, no theatres, no night clubs, no restaurants, no shops, not even a proper house for you to live in! You'll have to eat with your fingers and bath in the sea!'

'And sleep beneath the stars,' Lin said softly.

'I'll shake them out of the sky to make you a pillow,' Ruel promised her, and in their shared laughter she almost forgot the shadow that was April.

It was not until the next morning that her misgivings returned in full force. Ruel had gone to work, and she made up her mind to seek April out and to make one last bid to heal the breach between them. Even now she could not forget her promise to Aunt Bea, and she was desperately afraid that in her present mood April was capable of doing something really stupid.

'You've made your own bed, now you've got to lie on it,' Aunt Bea had been fond of saying, but Lin had never seen why the bed shouldn't be remade. It wasn't too late, even now, for April to put her past mistakes behind her. Not of course, if she threw in her lot with Luis Cortes, as Ruel seemed to think she might. That could only lead to disaster.

It took considerable courage for her to knock at April's door, for she was almost certain that she would meet with a rude reception. There was no answer to her knock, but she could hear someone moving about and also the sound of drawers being opened and shut. It also sounded as though the someone might be in a hurry. Lin frowned, and knocked again.

'April! Are you there?' she called. 'It's me— Lin. Can I come in?'

The door opened and April confronted her. Looking beyond her, Lin saw that the room was in a state of wild confusion. Drawers had been emptied on to the floor, there was a litter of clothes on the bed, and half-filled suitcases seemed to be everywhere.

'April! You're not going away?'

April looked at her. In the strong morning light she looked older . . . almost haggard, and there were black circles round her eyes. She seemed a different person from the angry termagant who had hurled abuse at her only a few hours earlier.

She said flatly, 'Yes. There's not much point in staying, is there? This isn't my home any longer. I don't suppose it will be too long before it's yours.' She turned away to light the inevitable cigarette. 'I really ought to congratulate you, coz. 'You've played your cards well.'

Lin winced. 'April . . .'

April gave her a twisted smile. 'I said some pretty horrid things to you last night, didn't I? In fact, I suppose I've behaved rather badly to you all the way along.' She sighed. 'It isn't much good saying I'm sorry. Even if you forgave me Ruel never would.' She gave a short laugh. 'I wish you joy of that one, coz. Personally I'd as soon be married to an armadillo, but I suppose there's no accounting for tastes.'

Lin said pleadingly, 'April, don't go away. Please. Stay a few days longer and take time to think what you're doing.'

April made a wry face. 'If I stay much longer I shall probably wake up one day to find I'm in jail. You're too late, my love. I'm going away with Luis this afternoon. We sail at twelve-thirty precisely.' She glanced at her watch. 'Needless to say we aren't sailing from Scarborough. Inspector Bailey might have something to say about that: he's rather expecting me to present myself at the police station like a repentant sinner.'

Lin's lips went dry. 'You're running away? With Luis?'

'Too true. He's picking me up at a deserted spot —your Mareo Bay, Lin.' She gave another brittle little laugh. 'That's shows what confidence I have in you, coz. I know you'd never give me away. I hope dear Ruel appreciates what a loyal little help-mate he's going to have beside him during the long years ahead.'

Lin hardly heard the mockery in her voice, certainly it didn't register.

She said desperately, using the only line of argument she thought might appeal, 'April, what about Godfrey's estate? You're entitled to that! If you go away—'

'Darling, I'm not going to worry about a few hundreds! Losing that lawsuit meant that Godfrey was practically beggared, didn't you know?' April put up her hand and patted her shining hair. 'Luckily Luis has got plenty for us both.' She paused, then added softly, 'Even though I may not go to him completely empty-handed.'

'What do you mean?' Lin sounded uncertain.

April laughed. 'Nothing, coz. Nothing at all.' She glanced at her watch again. 'And now—if you'll excuse me—I haven't much time. I don't want to keep Luis waiting. Nor would it be wise, under the circumstances!'

Lin turned and went away without another word, her heart heavy with foreboding. April was making a dreadful mistake, but there was nothing she could do about it. Perhaps if she telephoned Ruel . . . or the police . . . She shook her head, dismissing the idea immediately it entered her mind. She couldn't give April away, even for her ultimate good. Somehow she would have to work out her own salvation.

She wandered restlessly to the window and stood looking out at the sky. It was a fresh, blowy morning with a surprising amount of cloud. She wondered if Ruel would be able to get home for lunch. He had promised to do so if he possibly could, and she was in a fever of suppressed impatience to see him. How would he react to April's departure? Would he say that she should have tried to prevent it . . . or would he merely say 'Good riddance'? There was so much yet she had to learn about him . . . but thank goodness she had all her life in which to do it!

A slight noise in the next room startled her and she turned her head. It couldn't be Mandy . . . she'd gone out with Ruel. She could hear Aunt Lou singing in the kitchen, making herself heard even above the noise of the wireless, and Joseph, as usual, was working in the garden. Subconsciously she noted that the wind must be very strong . . . it was shaking the branches of the trees and there were a number of leaves scurrying along the grass.

There it was again! Lin frowned. It must be April . . . but if so she had come downstairs very quietly. Usually one heard the click-clack of her high heels on the polished wood. Was she going to slip out of the house without even saying goodbye?

She went quickly to the door of the sitting room and then froze into immobility, horrified by what she saw. April was standing by the open safe, and in her hand was something bright and glittering. Diamonds . . . Mandy's diamond necklace!

April looked up and saw her, and on her face was an expression of mingled shock, guilt and defiance. Then she gave a little shrug and slipped the diamonds into the pocket of her white tailored suit.

Lin leant against the door for support. Through shaking lips she whispered 'April, those diamonds . . . they're Mandy's! You're not . . . stealing them?'

April's face was set and hard. 'If you like to put it that way—yes, I am. I told you I wouldn't be going to Luis empty-handed, coz. These diamonds are worth a fortune, and I think I'm entitled to some compensation for twelve months of married boredom!'

'You can't do it!' Lin's voice was a cry of despair. 'April, you're already in trouble with the police! They'll catch you—'

'Oh no, they won't!' April's voice was soft. 'I'm relying on you, Lin dear. Ruel won't prosecute—not if you persuade him not to!'

Lin was ice-cold. She said desperately, 'They're all that Mandy has got belonging to her mother! I'm not going to let you take them, April! Put those diamonds back or you don't leave the house!'

'Won't I?' Suddenly April was across the room, pushing Lin out of the way so violently that she fell awkwardly, sprawling headlong across the floor. With a little gasp of triumph April was out of the room and Lin heard the door slam behind her and the sound of the key in the lock.

'April!' In a flash she was on her feet, pummelling at the door with futile hands. 'April! Come back!'

There was no answer. Shouting at the top of her voice, Lin yelled desperately for Aunt Lou. Not, she thought, despairingly, that she was likely to hear her—apart from the fact that she was slightly deaf, the wireless was on much too loud.

She heard the sound of a car starting up and hesitated no longer. Taking off her shoe, she smashed the window, stepping out into the garden amid a welter of broken glass just in time to see April's car disappearing round the bend in the drive.

The phone . . . She ran through the front door and into the hall, picking the receiver up with hands that were clumsy and trembled. The line was dead. Looking down, she saw why. No wonder April hadn't minded revealing her plans . . . she'd taken the precaution of cutting the wires. She must have laid her plans very carefully, Lin thought bitterly. Oh, if only it hadn't been *Mandy's* necklace! Nothing else would have mattered!

Aunt Lou came into the hall. She saw the open door—Lin had not waited to close it—and said with unusual sharpness ' You're not going out, Missy Lin?'

' I . . . was.' Lin gave her a wan smile. There was no transport available: to chase and catch April now was impossible.

' Best stay in. There's a hurricane warning,' Aunt Lou said stolidly. ' Might not hit us, but you never can tell. Where's Mrs Selby?'

Hurricane! Lin gasped. She had heard all about the hurricanes which were the only real scourge of the Caribbean isles . . . knew all about the devastation they caused to life and property!

Did Luis know? Anchored in that lonely bay, would he have heard the warning? Or would he and April set out for the open sea knowing nothing of the danger that faced them? She looked at her watch. ' We sail at twelve-thirty precisely . . .' In their haste to get away, would they ignore the strong wind that was blowing . . . be willing to take the risk that it might get worse?

She didn't stop to think any longer. Heedless of Aunt Lou's incredulous, horrified protest she ran out of the door and hatless, coatless, tore down the drive. Already the wind was terribly strong and the sky was grey and overcast. She set her lips. There *was* transport available . . . she'd forgotten about it till now and April must have forgotten it too. The old truck that Joseph sometimes used to bring things from town . . . oh, it was old, battered, in danger of falling to pieces, but it *went!* April had a good start, but she probably wouldn't go too fast,

believing as she did that she was safe from pursuit!
' If only I can get to the bay before they sail—warn
them!' Lin thought, and ' Please, please, please let
me be in time!'

Two or three minutes later she was speeding along
the road in the ancient truck. She could hear the
shriek of the wind even above the roar of the engine.
It seemed to be getting stronger every minute. The
road was deserted. ' Best stay in . . .' Lin remembered Aunt Lou's warning. Evidently most
people had the sense to ' stay in ' when there was a
hurricane warning!

The wind was lashing the trees this way and that
and she drove along in a shower of twigs and leaves.
Once a big branch came crashing down, missing the
bonnet of the truck by inches. Lin was beginning
to feel terrified . . . she'd never experienced a wind
like this before . . . but still she drove on. There
was just a chance . . . a slim one . . . that she would
be in time!

When she reached the bay she had almost to fight
her way down the cliff, battling against the wind all
the way. The air was colder than she had ever felt
it before in Tobago, and instead of the sea looking
calm and peaceful, as she remembered it, it was
grey and rough, and angry breakers were lashing
the reef.

She looked out to sea and gave a little cry of
despair. There was *Starlight*—she recognized the
boat's graceful lines. And April must be aboard . . .
her car was abandoned at the top of the cliff. She'd
arrived too late!

Wearily she struggled back to the road, with the

wind whipping at her hair, tearing at her clothes, lashing her face and trying to buffet her off her feet. She was icy cold now, but, she thought hopefully, the wind didn't seem to be any worse than when she set out. Perhaps it was just a violent, short-lived squall. Luis must think so, or surely he would never have put to sea!

Afterwards, she could never recall that nightmare drive home without a shudder of fear. The noise of the wind and the tossing trees was constantly in her ears and all around her branches were splintering off and crashing to the ground. They'd fallen on to the truck, too, but so far no damage had been done except for a badly cracked windscreen. If only a whole tree didn't fall on her perhaps she'd get home in safety . . . she'd only another mile or so to go.

Even as the thought crossed her mind there was a thunderous crash and the whole world was blotted out by a whirling storm of branches and leaves.

Warmth and comfort and the smell of disinfectant . . . and Ruel speaking her name. Lin surfaced from the darkness that had engulfed her and opened her eyes, for the second time in two days, to find Ruel bending over her, his face white and strained, his grey eyes anxious. Only this time she was in her own bedroom.

He said, and his voice sounded strangely gruff, 'How many lives have you got, Lin? Nine, like a cat?'

Then she remembered. She said weakly, 'I remember . . . the wind. Something fell . . .'

'A tree. A big one. Right on top of the truck.'

'How did I get out?'

'Somebody found you.' He paused and a slight shudder shook his broad frame. 'Apart from slight concussion, there wasn't a thing wrong with you. The truck's a wreck.' He smiled faintly. 'Your guardian angel has been putting in quite a lot of overtime on your behalf!'

For a few moments Lin lay very still. Ruel was watching her, his face quiet.

She said with difficulty, 'I went—after April. Aunt Lou said—there was a hurricane warning. She went—with Luis.'

Something in his expression warned her. For a moment he hesitated, as if debating whether it was kinder to tell her now or wait until later, then he spoke very gently.

'The yacht capsized, Lin. They've found the wreckage.'

'And—April?'

He did not answer, and Lin turned her face into the pillow. She felt Ruel's hand stroking her hair.

He said, 'They hadn't a chance, Lin. The wind suddenly veered and it must have hit them broadside on. Why Cortes took a chance, putting out to sea in a gale like that . . .' He shrugged helplessly.

Lin said wearily, 'It was the necklace. April took Mandy's diamonds. I tried to stop her, but I couldn't.'

There was a dull ache in her heart, but the tears would not come. It seemed dreadful not to be able to cry for April . . . but the girl who had set sail with Luis in *Starlight* hadn't been the April with whom she'd grown up. She'd been a stranger . . . a ruthless, calculating stranger. She'd gambled, and she'd lost, and she'd paid the price of failure.

Ruel put his arms round her and held her closely. She could feel his heart beating strongly against her cheek.

'It doesn't matter about the diamonds, Lin. Let the sea have them. What matters is that you're safe.' He kissed her tenderly. 'You've nothing to reproach yourself with, Lin. You've stuck by April through thick and thin—you even risked your own life to try and save her. Now she's a memory . . . and the last few days belong to the shadows. Are you going to live there too—or are you going to walk with me, in the sunshine?'

Ruel was right. As she returned his kiss Lin knew that yesterday had gone, and with it yesterday's sorrow. She had come to what she had thought of as an enchanted island and even now, after all that had happened, the impression remained. For she had learned one thing—that the only real enchantment was love.

F R E E ! ! !

Did you know . . . . ?

that just by mailing in the coupon below you can receive a brand new, up-to-date "Harlequin Romance Catalogue" listing literally hundreds of Harlequin Romances you probably thought were out of print.

Now you can shop in your own home for novels by your favorite Harlequin authors — the Essie Summers you wanted to read, the Violet Winspear you missed, the Mary Burchell you thought wasn't available anymore!

They're all listed in the "Harlequin Romance Catalogue". And something else too — the books are listed in numerical sequence, — so you can fill in the missing numbers in your library.

Don't delay — mail the coupon below to us today. We'll promptly send you the "Harlequin Romance Catalogue".

Have You Missed Any of These
Harlequin Romances?

- [ ] 427 NURSE BROOKES
  Kate Norway
- [ ] 438 MASTER OF SURGERY
  Alex Stuart
- [ ] 446 TO PLEASE THE DOCTOR
  Marjorie Moore
- [ ] 458 NEXT PATIENT, DOCTOR
  ANNE, Elizabeth Gilzean
- [ ] 468 SURGEON OF DISTINCTION
  Mary Burchell
- [ ] 469 MAGGY, Sara Seale
- [ ] 486 NURSE CARIL'S NEW POST
  Caroline Trench
- [ ] 487 THE HAPPY ENTERPRISE
  Eleanor Farnes
- [ ] 491 NURSE TENNANT
  Elizabeth Hoy
- [ ] 494 LOVE IS MY REASON
  Mary Burchell
- [ ] 495 NURSE WITH A DREAM
  Norrey Ford
- [ ] 503 NURSE IN CHARGE
  Elizabeth Gilzean
- [ ] 504 PETER RAYNAL, SURGEON
  Marjorie Moore
- [ ] 584 VILLAGE HOSPITAL
  Margaret Malcolm
- [ ] 599 RUN AWAY FROM LOVE
  Jean S. Macleod
  (Original Harlequin title
  "Nurse Companion")
- [ ] 631 DOCTOR'S HOUSE
  Dorothy Rivers
- [ ] 647 JUNGLE HOSPITAL
  Juliet Shore
- [ ] 672 GREGOR LOTHIAN, SURGEON
  Joan Blair
- [ ] 683 DESIRE FOR THE STAR
  Averil Ives
  (Original Harlequin title
  "Doctor's Desire")
- [ ] 744 VERENA FAYRE, PROBA-
  TIONER, Valerie K. Nelson
- [ ] 745 TENDER NURSE, Hilda Nickson
- [ ] 757 THE PALM-THATCHED
  HOSPITAL, Juliet Shore
- [ ] 758 HELPING DOCTOR MEDWAY
  Jan Haye
- [ ] 764 NURSE ANN WOOD
  Valerie K. Nelson

- [ ] 771 NURSE PRUE IN CEYLON
  Gladys Fullbrook
- [ ] 772 CHLOE WILDE, STUDENT
  NURSE, Joan Turner
- [ ] 787 THE TWO FACES OF NURSE
  ROBERTS, Nora Sanderson
- [ ] 790 SOUTH TO THE SUN
  Betty Beaty
- [ ] 794 SURGEON'S RETURN
  Hilda Nickson
- [ ] 812 FACTORY NURSE   Hilary Neal
- [ ] 825 MAKE UP YOUR MIND NURSE
  Phyllis Matthewman
- [ ] 841 TRUANT HEART
  Patricia Fenwick
  (Original Harlequin title
  "Doctor in Brazil")
- [ ] 858 MY SURGEON NEIGHBOUR
  Jane Arbor
- [ ] 873 NURSE JULIE OF WARD
  THREE   Joan Callender
- [ ] 878 THIS KIND OF LOVE
  Kathryn Blair
- [ ] 890 TWO SISTERS
  Valerie K. Nelson
- [ ] 897 NURSE HILARY'S HOLIDAY
  TASK, Jan Haye
- [ ] 900 THERE CAME A SURGEON
  Hilda Pressley
- [ ] 901 HOPE FOR TOMORROW
  Anne Weale
- [ ] 902 MOUNTAIN OF DREAMS
  Barbara Rowan
- [ ] 903 SO LOVED AND SO FAR
  Elizabeth Hoy
- [ ] 907 HOMECOMING HEART
  Joan Blair
  (Original Harlequin title
  "Two for the Doctor")
- [ ] 909 DESERT DOORWAY
  Pamela Kent
- [ ] 911 RETURN OF SIMON
  Celine Conway
- [ ] 912 THE DREAM AND THE
  DANCER, Eleanor Farnes
- [ ] 919 DEAR INTRUDER
  Jane Arbor
- [ ] 936 TIGER HALL
  Esther Wyndham

Have You Missed Any of These
Harlequin Romances?

☐ 1246 THE CONSTANT HEART
Eleanor Farnes
☐ 1248 WHERE LOVE IS
Norrey Ford
☐ 1253 DREAM COME TRUE
Patricia Fenwick
☐ 1276 STEEPLE RIDGE
Jill Tahourdin
☐ 1277 STRANGER'S TRESPASS
Jane Arbor
☐ 1282 THE SHINING STAR
Hilary Wilde
☐ 1284 ONLY MY HEART TO GIVE
Nan Asquith
☐ 1288 THE LAST OF THE KINTYRES
Catherine Airlie
☐ 1293 I KNOW MY LOVE
Sara Seale
☐ 1309 THE HILLS OF MAKETU
Gloria Bevan
☐ 1312 PEPPERCORN HARVEST
Ivy Ferrari
☐ 1601 THE NEWCOMER
Hilda Pressley
☐ 1607 NOT LESS THAN ALL
Margaret Malcolm
☐ 1718 LORD OF THE FOREST
Hilda Nickson
☐ 1722 FOLLOW A STRANGER
Charlotte Lamb
☐ 1725 THE EXTRAORDINARY EN-
GAGEMENT   Marjorie Lewty
☐ 1726 MAN IN CHARGE, Lilian Peake
☐ 1729 THE YOUNG DOCTOR
Sheila Douglas
☐ 1730 FLAME IN FIJI, Gloria Bevan
☐ 1731 THE FORBIDDEN VALLEY
Essie Summers
☐ 1732 BEYOND THE SUNSET
Flora Kidd
☐ 1733 CALL AND I'LL COME
Mary Burchell
☐ 1734 THE GIRL FROM ROME
Nan Asquith
☐ 1735 TEMPTATIONS OF THE MOON
Hilary Wilde
☐ 1736 THE ENCHANTED RING
Lucy Gillen

☐ 1737 WINTER OF CHANGE
Betty Neels
☐ 1738 THE MUTUAL LOOK
Joyce Dingwell
☐ 1739 BELOVED ENEMY
Mary Wibberley
☐ 1740 ROMAN SUMMER
Jane Arbor
☐ 1741 MOORLAND MAGIC
Elizabeth Ashton
☐ 1743 DESTINY IS A FLOWER
Stella Frances Nel
☐ 1744 WINTER LOVING
Janice Gray
☐ 1745 NURSE AT NOONGWALLA
Roumelia Lane
☐ 1746 WITHOUT ANY AMAZEMENT
Margaret Malcolm
☐ 1748 THE GOLDEN MADONNA
Rebecca Stratton
☐ 1749 LOVELY IS THE ROSE
Belinda Dell
☐ 1750 THE HOUSE OF THE SCISSORS
Isobel Chace
☐ 1751 CARNIVAL COAST
Charlotte Lamb
☐ 1752 MIRANDA'S MARRIAGE
Margery Hilton
☐ 1753 TIME MAY CHANGE
Nan Asquith
☐ 1754 THE PRETTY WITCH
Lucy Gillen
☐ 1755 SCHOOL MY HEART
Penelope Walsh
☐ 1756 AN APPLE IN EDEN
Kay Thorpe
☐ 1757 THE GIRL AT SALTBUSH FLAT
Dorothy Cork
☐ 1758 THE CRESCENT MOON
Elizabeth Hunter
☐ 1759 THE REST IS MAGIC
Marjorie Lewty
☐ 1760 THE GUARDED GATES
Katrina Britt
☐ 1780 THE TOWER OF THE WINDS
Elizabeth Hunter
☐ 1783 CINDERELLA IN MINK
Roberta Leigh